From Margate to Key West with Love

Time flies – virtue alone remains

Sally Forrester

BookLocker
Trenton, Georgia

Disclaimer

This book details the author's personal experiences with and opinions about Bach flower essences, homeopathic remedies and maintaining a healthy lifestyle. The author is a Registered Homeopath MARH (UK) a Registered Bach Flower Essence Practitioner. BFRP and a licensed massage therapist and reflexologist in the state of Florida.

The author and publisher are providing this book and its contents on an "as is" basis and make no representations or warranties of any kind with respect to this book or its contents. The author and publisher disclaim all such representations and warranties, including for example warranties of merchantability and healthcare for a particular purpose. In addition, the author and publisher do not represent or warrant that the information accessible via this book is accurate, complete or current.

The statements made about products and services are not intended to diagnose, treat, cure, or prevent any condition or disease. Please consult with your own physician or healthcare specialist regarding the suggestions and recommendations made in this book.

Except as specifically stated in this book, neither the author or publisher, nor any authors, contributors, or other representatives will be liable for damages arising out of or in connection with the use of this book. This is a comprehensive limitation of liability that applies to all damages of any kind, including (without limitation) compensatory; direct, indirect or consequential damages; loss of data, income or profit; loss of or damage to property and claims of third parties.

You understand that this book is not intended as a substitute for consultation with a licensed healthcare practitioner, such as your physician. Before you begin any healthcare program, or change your lifestyle in any way, you will consult your physician or other licensed healthcare practitioner to ensure that you are in good health and that the examples contained in this book will not harm you.

This book provides content related to topics physical and/or mental health issues. As such, use of this book implies your acceptance of this disclaimer.

For James, Giles, Lauren
And Frank

I would rather be a superb meteor, every atom of me in magnificent glow, than a sleepy and permanent planet. The proper function of man is to live not to exist.

I shall not waste my days in trying to prolong them.
I shall use my time.

Jack London

Author's Note – Summer 2022

I was first drawn to the Florida Keys in the late 1970's. Cliff and I had recently married and we took a holiday trip to Florida and the Bahamas. It was while we were sunning ourselves in Miami that we decided to take a drive down to the Florida Keys. In those days the tourist industry had yet to explode. I just recall this very long road with ocean either side and a number of small business establishments and houses strung out along what seemed like a never-ending highway. That first adventure took us as far as Key Largo in the Upper Keys. As time moved on, we made more trips to the Keys eventually making our way to Key West at the end of the road.

In those earlier days we flew because Cliff had a private pilot's license. Flying in a four seat Cessna aircraft relatively low over the Florida Keys was a truly magical experience. They reminded me of a pearl necklace strung out and surrounded by azure ocean. I was fascinated by all the bridges linked by tiny strips of land. It was not until much later in life that I really began to comprehend and acknowledge the enormous feat of engineering that had created Henry Flagler's vision. His concrete railway arches built in mainly shallow water are still visible today. Some dubbed it *Flagler's Folly* and others viewed the 127 - mile Florida Overseas Railroad as the *Eighth Wonder of the World*. Of course, Flagler's Railroad has been long gone. The devastating hurricane of 1935 wrecked a good part of it tragically hammering the nail in its coffin.

When our two sons, James and Giles, were quite grown up and flown from the family nest Cliff and I embarked upon yet more adventures of exploration on our Catalina 38-foot sailing yacht aptly named, *Risk Taker*. When we purchased her, she'd already sailed to many exotic ports of call enroute from San Francisco and transiting the Panama Canal. *Risky* continued for a further six years sailing throughout South America. Sadly, earlier this year, we had to let our old lady go. We both realized that she'd become too much for us to handle. Thankfully the precious lady that had kept us so safe in very bad weather still had a lot more life left in her. Cliff had recently rebuilt her Kubota engine and we'd both spent many hours over the years ensuring that she was kept in first class condition. I'm happy to report that she's found new owners, a younger couple from Mexico, who seem to love her as much as we did and they're planning yet more sailing adventures.

It was in *Risky* that we really came to know the Florida Keys, particularly Key West and the Dry Tortugas. In the spring of 2021, we spent a month at the Stock Island Marina and it was during that particular sojourn that I became so inspired with the quirky city at the end of the road. I just knew in my heart that I wanted to write a book. Cliff and I had the opportunity to explore the down town area in depth and we came to really appreciate the colourful history of this city at the end of the road.

Of course, it's a tourist destination and until Covid hit many of the cruise ships would pull into the harbour making the city literally bulge at the seams! However, once one strays from Duval Street, the heart of the town, with its the sleezy T shirt shops, bars including Sloppy Joe's, a favourite of Ernest Hemingway, all the heavy drinking and the Margaritaville atmosphere there's an alluring magic to be found in Old Key West. Its narrow streets are lined with old wood frame houses and a profusion of tropical trees such as mango and avocado. There are flowering, exotic plants bursting with colour and beautiful sweet perfumes. Being so close to Cuba and having interesting historical connections with that Caribbean Island there's definitely a Cuban, Latin atmosphere. Many of the restaurants serve Cuban food. Cliff and I found a favourite place out on Stock Island called *El Siboney* where we spent many memorable evenings and grew to love the Cuban cuisine. Then there's the chickens roaming freely and the old roosters who can be heard crowing early in the morning and at sundown to summon their harem into the trees and bushes for the night.

From Margate to Key West with Love is a continuation of my previous three historical novels featuring Madam Maria Popoff, her quirky vintage dress shop set in Margate's King Street and Poppy, a middle-aged woman, who relocates from London to Margate. Poppy, who has many broken pieces, discovers true healing when she answers an advertisement requesting part time help although *only special people needed to apply!*

My novels, although works of fiction, embrace the ups and downs of life, of truly being human, of living through and navigating difficult times and the important part that emotions play in sickness and recovery. They're set in various historical periods that follow real events.

Having spent some time sailing to the Florida Keys, exploring Key West and learning about its checkered history I just knew that I wanted Maria Popoff to come and establish yet another vintage shop. Cousin Rollo has summoned her to the fictitious grand old house called *St. Eustace* on Whitehead Street in the heart of Old Key West. Maria brings her wisdom, knowledge, love, compassion and her all seeing eyes to this colourful settlement at the very end of the road.

Maria Popoff is certainly a strange character and it's never really clear exactly who she is. Some see her merely as a kind, particularly old and portly shopkeeper who has a passion for decadent chocolate cake. Those who know her better are struck by her all-seeing eyes that seem to pierce right through you. They're struck by her wisdom, her knowledge of healing and fascinated by her wizened hands that can touch and seemingly make everything better. Some have called her a gypsy who has the power to look through a crystal ball and foretell the future. However, those who know her best of all realize that she's a time traveller or maybe she's an angel. Certainly, she's an ancient being who appears to cross the dimension of time.

Maria has seen so much. She's become weary of man's indiscretion, his mistakes and of the lessons that humanity never seems to learn. Set in 2021 and 2022 Maria, like most of us, is worried about the state of our planet. She has a heartfelt concern for the environment, pollution and the devastating weather patterns that seem to track man's hatred and violence towards each other. Maria is horrified by the war in Ukraine. She realizes just how much sorrow the Covid pandemic has wrought robbing people of their loved ones, their sense of financial security, and their livelihoods.

I wanted my fourth novel to span the Atlantic so that my readers will also happily discover Poppy still busy in the Isle of Thanet managing all three Madam Popoff vintage shops in the little seaside holiday towns of Margate, Ramsgate and Broadstairs. Things come into the shops that have a story to tell. Poppy has become proficient, over the years, at fingering certain treasures catching her eye and she discovers their past. Sometimes the stories are heartwarming and pleasant but just like life they don't always have a fairy tale ending. Likewise, Maria has taught Desmond, a new employee, to sit with things that appear on the doorstep of *St. Eustace* and discover their history. In this way I bring to light all sorts of historical events that have shaped the community across the Atlantic at the very end of the road. Readers will enjoy stories embracing Key West's past. Sunken Spanish treasure, sponging, cigar factories, historic links with Cuba, Flagler's Railroad, hurricanes, First World War submarines and much more.

Above all my books have a purpose. They're much more than the sum of historical fiction featuring an old lady who has a passion for chocolate cake and set in vintage dress shops! I love to educate. Starting out in life as a school teacher but over time, becoming older and wiser, I've learnt so much about the nature of healing and this knowledge is woven into my books. Nowadays I write, paint and coach people in wellness. Homeopathic remedies and Bach flower essences have been my passion for nearly twenty-five years and I love to share my knowledge with all of my readers. I invite my readers to come and take afternoon tea with Madam Popoff and Poppy and become enlightened.

Please enjoy my latest novel and remember that all my stories are works of fiction as are the characters but there are also many nuggets of knowledge and true historical details to be gained. The real Madam Popoff Vintage is a delightful place, situated at number 4, King Street

Margate. Several years ago, I was browsing in the shop and while among the racks of vintage frocks it suddenly occurred to me that I could write a work of fiction based upon this quirky shop. The real Madam Popoff, Deborah, is a lovely lady and if you would like to know more about her real establishment then please visit her web site.

https://madampopoffvintage.patternbyetsy.com

For Sally Forrester's other books

Last Train to Margate

Ramsgate Calling

Broadstairs on my Mind

Please visit www.sallyforrester.com

Hilaree, many
thanks for all that
you do for homeopathy!
Warm wishes
Sally
March '23

A New Beginning:

St. Eustace - Front of House

Maria Popoff always had friends in America for as long as she could remember. She recalled memories of ancient relatives residing in far-off Key West. It's that quirky township at the end of Highway 1 where the poster board in town announces:

End of the Rainbow

The urgent message to pack up her bags, leave her beloved Isle of Thanet and relocate to the end of the road had come in a dream. The planet was in trouble, America was in trouble and Florida was in a lot of trouble. The Delta variant of the Coronavirus was ravaging the state. *Help needed, go quickly* continually played like a broken record in Maria's mind. Finally, she felt that it was time to act.

Maria, mysterious, portly and wizened by age found herself on the doorstep of her elderly cousin Rollo. "Maria, welcome! You've come at long last to Key West to hold the light!" The equally wizened old man chuckled as he opened the large oak door to his beautiful historic home set amongst palm trees, fragrant tropical flowers and colourful bougainvillea overlooking the sparkling blue ocean.

Maria sat down. She was tired and felt the weight of the whole world rested upon her bent old shoulders. Rollo busied himself in the kitchen and reappeared with a tray of tea and her favourite chocolate cake. "Maria, I've been waiting patiently for you to come and now at long last you're finally here, welcome." His glassy blue eyes smiled with happiness and a great sense of relief. Rollo knew that with Maria by his side there was hope. They were both time travellers, ancient wise beings helping humanity to set a more favourable course. "Maria, we're in a lot of trouble. All this talk of global warming is so concerning. There have been such erratic weather patterns lately. So much rain and flooding then all this extreme heat and those forest fires. Add in pollution, toxic environments and sick suffering people everywhere. There's all the hatred, violence and general unrest. To add to this growing mountain of problems we've this Delta variant to contend with." Maria looked up from her teacup with weary glazed eyes and mumbled, "Cousin Rollo what do you want me to do? Why am I here in Key West? Of course, it's better known for fishing, turtling, sponging wrecking and salvage. Then I recall there were the cigar factories, processing salt plants, housing for the military, smuggling and of course in more recent times tourism. Why do you specifically need me here?"

"Maria, we can and will accomplish a lot together. As with everywhere across the globe the people here need our help. We have to start somewhere. You throw a pebble in the pond and it has a ripple effect. Together we can start to influence a change for the better. We will be the influencers." Maria smiled; she liked that word influencer. She knew all about the young influencers on YouTube and all the fashionistas who had huge followings. So, influencers for the good sounded a wonderful idea. "So, Cousin Rollo, how can we possibly pull it off?" Rollo straightened up, looked Maria directly in the eye and said, "Doing what you're good at Maria, hospitality and helpful guidance. People need your attention, your time, your love and those old wizened hands that exude such remarkable healing energy."

Maria's arrival in Key West coincided with yet another earthquake striking an already fractured Haiti and made even worse by Tropical Storm Grace. The Taliban had marched into Kabul, that last bastion of safety for so many desperate people from Afghanistan and there was total chaos at the airport as people struggled to leave. An unsettled, troubled world was watching and waiting and many people were actually asking the question, "Is this the end of times?"

Cousin Rollo, sensing Maria's sadness, rose and pulled out a large colourful folder from an antique roll top desk. "Maria I've a very special place for your sojourn here in Key West. Old friends recently passed over and bequeathed to me a very large and beautiful Victorian home down near the harbour it's called St. Eustace. It's the perfect place for you to set up shop, expand your vintage emporium business, and there's room for me to tinker in the numerous garages and workshops that once upon a time were stables. Together we can create a place for healing and reconciliation. St. Eustace will in time become a Key West landmark."

After supper Maria retired early and following a deep and restful sleep, she was ready to accompany Cousin Rollo to inspect the grand house. Today she felt more like her best self. Feeling more refreshed there was a spring in her step. Actually, the sight of St. Eustace came as no surprise when they arrived in Whitehead Street where the stunningly beautiful home nestled amongst a wide variety of colourful tropical plants and Royal Poinciana Trees. Maria gasped, "Why, I've seen it so many times before in my dreams! This beautiful place has always been calling me, beckoning for me to come!" Indeed, the large house was beautiful, one of those imposing yet picturesque places eagerly photographed by all the visitors who pass through Key West every year. It was set back in large, well-cared for tropical gardens, manicured lawns, and surrounded by exquisitely ornate wrought iron railings. These railings had been fashioned to incorporate beautiful images of botanical flowers and foliage. There were creatures of the forest too. Birds, hares, squirrels, deer, and even a tortoise had been carefully crafted from the wrought iron. The mainly wooden clad house was painted white. There were bright green louvered shutters framing the windows many of which were of stained-glass depicting woodland scenery. A large wrap around porch painted white surrounded the house at ground level and there was another porch around the upper story. It featured a carved pineapple design that enduring symbol of southern hospitality. At one end of the home stood a tall faded red brick turret and looking up one could see atop the lofty tower a weather vane shaped into the image of a fleeing golden hind.

Cousin Rollo took Maria's hand as they both gazed at the lovely mansion. "St. Eustace became known as the patron saint of hunters and firefighters and also of anyone facing adversity. Come Maria, we'll take a look inside and decide how we can be ready to open the doors on September 20th the traditional feast day of St. Eustace."

The old house was cavernous and in an excellent state of repair. Maria immediately fell in love with the spacious wrap around porch with its high ceiling fans and glazed deep blue Grecian urns over filled with colourful exotic tropical plants. She visualized an array of elegant wicker patio furniture and happy customers enjoying afternoon tea and fancy cakes served on fine bone china. Her quick and lively mind began to see so many possibilities. The interior exuded a certain elegance and it was obvious that the previous owners had deeply loved and cared for their property. There was a very large modern kitchen; Maria noticed the pretty blue delft tiles on the walls depicting windmills and country scenes. She immediately began to ponder the possibility of operating a tea party café cum vintage boutique.

St. Eustace with its polished oak floors, high ceiling fans and exquisite stained-glass windows was a gift. "Cousin Rollo do tell me about the friends who bequeathed this marvellous treasure to you." Rollo sighed and smiled, "Well, that's a very long story but I will make it simple. Dick and Dolly were very fine citizens of this troubled planet. Honest, hardworking, generous people who built up their successful jewellery business from scratch. Dick was a talented gold and silversmith and Dolly was a fine artist. They purchased the dilapidated house once called Sea View from the estate of an old sea captain. They managed to save it from demolition. Squatters had occupied the property for a number of years, mainly homeless drug users. Dick and Dolly spent years lovingly restoring it to its former Victoria glory. In fact, it was a work in progress for over 20 years. Of course, they were in the fortunate position to have the necessary finances to afford some of the best craftsmen in the south. I first encountered the couple after the tragic death of their only child, David. I clearly remember how terribly distraught they both were. The couple had sought out many healers and eventually fate led them to my doorstep. David died in a terrible forest fire. He loved nature and had gone to work as a forest warden somewhere far up north. About 25 years ago there was a lightning strike one sultry summer's evening and the forest where he was living and working caught light. That fire took away David's life along with many others who tried in vain to quench the flames.

Actually St. Eustace was my idea. You know that he's the patron saint of fire fighters. I encouraged Dick and Dolly to channel their energy into creating something beautiful, a testament to David's memory and his love of nature, especially the trees and woodland animals. If you look carefully, you'll see many different types of wood used throughout the property. David's parents engaged the finest carpenters and stained-glass experts. Dolly designed many of the glass woodland scenes herself. She always used to say that she could feel her David's presence near to her when she was in the house. As the couple grew older, they became more and more concerned as to the fate of St. Eustace following their passing. Before he died Dick told me that they'd decided to bequeath the house to me. Apparently, I was the healer who'd helped them the most to deal with and to transform their profound grief into something more positive and sustainable. They trusted St. Eustace to me upon their demise requesting that it should become a safe haven for equally troubled souls. Their passing was probably a lot sooner than they imagined. This terrible Coronavirus took them both earlier this year, they were in their mid-eighties. It's taken many months to get all the paper work sorted but now I'm officially the keeper of St. Eustace. Maria, this is why I have called you to Key West. Together we can respect Dick and Dolly's wish and fulfil their legacy, after all it's what we both do best. We help people to mend all their broken pieces."

Maria smiled and chuckled, "This special place was created by love. I can feel the walls exuding that welcoming all-embracing energy. Cousin Rollo you and I can do good work here. Maybe our best work yet! There's plenty of room for all of my vintage paraphernalia. I see a bustling little café operating out of the large dining room and if the weather permits the spacious wrap around porch will be a fine place to take morning coffee and afternoon tea. There's even room for me to rest upstairs but what about you? What part do you play in this new adventure?" Smiling Rollo replied, "Maria men need a place to come and share their worries too. They need a safe place to confide, even a place to weep without judgment. St. Eustace has many workshops and garages out in the back. Dick had the old stables converted. He was a fine gold and silversmith and all of his specialist equipment still remains. There are also three classic cars purchased over his lifetime but somehow, he never found the time to refurbish and get them back on the road. It's my plan to head up the tinker shop. Everyone will be welcome to come and help out, share their skills, learn, make new friends, and build a community. We'll offer classes and maybe even take in donated vehicles that can be serviced and redistributed to people in need. Heavens knows this Covid crisis has affected so many people in different ways. Some will come for comfort and healing, some to simply learn a new skill or to make friends but some will surely stay forever! I've many friends in town. They're garage owners, skilled mechanics, metal workers, and jewellers. I'm sure they'll be happy to pitch in and lend a hand in return for the many favours they've received from old Rollo over the years."

Maria smiled. Margate felt so very far away, all of her vintage businesses were now in Poppy's safe and capable hands. The idea of yet another beginning in Key West didn't seem such a bad idea after all. "Come Cousin Rollo there's much to be done before we open the doors of St. Eustace on September 20th 2021."

When one has a plan and walks in step with universal law all manner of things happens for the greater good. Rollo happened to know all the right people at City Hall to expedite a café license especially since Maria proposed to keep things very simple. St. Eustace would serve morning coffee and pastries and offer simple afternoon tea, dainty cakes and freshly baked scones. Arrangements were made with a local bakery to supply a daily offering of good quality pastries and dainty cakes including gluten free and vegan options. However, Maria insisted that her very special chocolate cake and fruit scones should be baked daily in the kitchen. She posted an advert in several local papers and magazines.

Local vintage emporium, tea cafe and workshop seek help. The grand opening is on September 20th. Only special people need apply. Address all enquiries to St. Eustace.

Cousin Rollo once complained, "Maria we really need to include the full address so that people know exactly where to find us." Maria gently took his hand and looked deep into his sparkling blue eyes, "Cousin Rollo you should know by now that those requiring our help and those who are compelled to come and join us in this grand adventure will surely find us, St. Eustace is enough!" Rollo threw back his head and laughed, "Of course you're right!"

Maria Popoff, the wise old women whom Poppy could never figure out, was as always right. A few days later following the placement of her adverts there was a loud rap at the enormous oak door surrounded by stained glass panels of woodland creatures. Maria found herself looking down upon two equally ancient African American ladies. They were dressed in colourful Caribbean print dresses with matching turbans. Troubled by painful arthritic hips and knees they stood bent over leaning on walking sticks. However, when they turned their wizened faces up and towards Maria, they almost blinded her with their radiant smile and the love that seemed to ooze from every fibre of their being. Nothing was said. Maria beckoned for them to come in and it was only when they were settled at a table in the dining room and sipping coffee from elegant gold rimmed bone china cups that the conversations begun.

They were sisters, Bella and Harriet, lifelong Key West residents and descendants of a freed black slave from Georgia who'd come to the Keys to work on Henry Flagler's railroad. Bella spoke first in a lyrical southern accent, "Folk at the Missionary Baptist Church told us that you were looking for help. Of course, we're very old, retired from a lifetime of hard work but boredom has set in. Truth is there's life in us yet and the good Lord said that we should come so here we are!" Maria sighed, smiled and taking each sister by the hand she said, "Indeed so, St. Eustace has been waiting for you both. Welcome! You'll find a purpose here, there's much to be done but tell me what gift do you ladies bring to this special place?" Harriet put down her coffee cup and placing her old wrinkled hands on the table she said, "Look here at my hands. They've done much work, enough for many lifetimes but always God's work. We're dressmakers. We started out in our teens in an apprenticeship. That was way back in 1952. We can make all kinds of garments. Friends at church call us the queens of the sewing machine. We heard you're creating a vintage store and we know that young people these days are all interested in clothes from the 1940's - 1960's. We can easily make those fashions to order. We just want somewhere to come, to be around folk, help out, and be of some use. It's not about money although a donation to our church would be greatly appreciated!"

Bella continued the conversation by adding, "We're also mothers and grandmothers. We've raised 12 children between us. We've known both good and bad times; the joy of new life and the loss when loved ones have left us. We're both widows, our children are all grown up, most of the grandchildren too. We both know what it's like to be human. We've experienced many ups and downs and we know that this world is deeply troubled. We want our twilight years to have meaning. Sitting at home in the rocking chair is not for us! It was Grace that sent us here so please can we stay?"

Maria threw back her head and laughing she said, "Of course you can stay I've just the place for you to set up a little workshop!" She escorted the two sisters to a smaller room adjacent to the large dining room and kitchen. It had beautiful stained-glass windows that overlooked the wrap around porch and there were two high ceiling fans. The walls were painted a delicate pink. There was a large collection of watercolour paintings on the wall. These were collected by Dolly over the years and depicted country scenes of ancient hill top villages and fields of lavender and sunflowers in faraway France and Italy. These were vacation places visited by Dick and Dolly in their younger years. There was an antique chaise longue and a comfortable armchair in one corner, a large costume mirror in another and a huge polished oak table in the centre that would be ideal to lay out their fabric and patterns. Bella and Harriet were ecstatic and couldn't wait to share their successful visit to St. Eustace with their friends. Maria asked them to bring along their beloved Singer sewing machines so that they could start to make frocks before the grand opening on September 20th. She promised to have bolts of material ready for them within a few days and that half of all sales would be donated to their church and any profit remaining would be used to fund the charitable community work that St. Eustace would be conducting in the near future.

Once Bella and Harriet had set things in motion many things began to happen all at once. Pastor Joe and a helper from the Missionary Baptist Church arrived the very next day in a large, old, beaten up, yellow school bus. They unloaded two very ancient looking Singer sewing machines set inside their own special tables. They also carried several wicker baskets filled with scissors, pins, tailors chalk, and brightly coloured threads and ribbons that the two sisters had collected over a lifetime of sewing. Maria invited the two men to step inside out of the heat and to sit down in the dining room. She hurried into the kitchen and brought out a large tray of lemonade and slices of her homemade chocolate cake. Cousin Rollo joined them and they shared the grand plans that they had in mind for St. Eustace. Pastor Joe was particularly grateful that Bella and Harriet had found a new purpose. He confided that he'd worried about the two elderly sisters for some time. He talked about the toll that Coronavirus had taken on all their community; it had hit the African American population hard. His parishioners had suffered much loss not only of their loved ones but the economic fallout was particularly devastating. "Many people can no longer afford their living expenses. We've got long lines at our soup kitchen every day. Hard working people are hungry," Joe moaned.

That evening Maria and Cousin Rollo discussed how St. Eustace could help the many suffering people that Pastor Joe had brought to their attention. The idea of a lunchtime soup kitchen for the hungry seemed like a good idea and something that was definitely within the realms of possibility. It was still the topic of conversation the next day when Ruth arrived on the doorstep. Maria had been out and about gathering bolts of material so that Bella and Harriet could get started with their sewing projects. Ruth was sitting in a rocking chair on the wrap around porch and waiting for her. "Hello, I've been here for some time waiting and wondering. I saw your advert." Maria smiled and held out her hand to welcome the newcomer then she sat down on the rocking chair next to Ruth and they began to chat. Ruth was in her early 50's. She was tall, trim, athletic and very tanned. She struck Maria as being a tough, capable, no-nonsense type of a person. "I've travelled the world for so long now. I'm a sailor. I live on an old boat in the harbour and work part time on Friday, Saturday and Sunday on the tall ships. There are several historic schooners in the harbour. They're tourist attractions although business isn't so good at this time of the year because it's far too hot and there's little wind. Then there's the violent thunderstorms that come in the late afternoon most days. I help out on the deck and I'm in charge of the catering. That means organizing sandwiches and cold drinks for the day sails and serving snacks, wine and cocktails on the evening sunset sailings. I went to cookery school in my late teens then took off to travel and work my way around the world. Funny, I never really found a home. My elderly parents are still around. They still live up north in Maine where I grew up. I ended up in Key West three years ago. Before that I worked on the island of Antigua. I'm definitely searching but I'm not exactly sure what for. However, your interesting advert caught my eye. I can turn my hand to most things, I'm hardworking and reliable. It's strange but I'm sure I've seen this house before. Of course, I'm familiar with the home because I often pass it on my way to the stores since I've lived here in Key West. However, years ago in far off Antigua, a house kept appearing in my dreams and it looked just like this place. How very strange!"

Maria laughed, "Ruth, my dear, you've definitely been called here and St. Eustace has apparently been waiting for your arrival. Maybe you will find the peace you've been searching for and somewhere to really call home. I need a cook. It's my plan to offer morning coffee and afternoon tea. I need someone to help serve and who can bake scones and my special chocolate cake recipe. Cousin Rollo and I've just been talking about the possibility of a lunchtime soup kitchen for the hungry. Can you manage that too?" Ruth smiled she liked the look of this kindly old woman, "Yes, I can do all of that. I can see if the schooner business can do without me on Fridays. We're very slack right now so I can probably be here Monday through Friday to cook and serve."

As Maria rose up from her rocking chair Ruth suddenly turned to face her and said, "Maria, there's one condition. I must bring Henry." Maria turned, looked her in the eye and enquired, "Who's this, Henry?" Ruth laughed, "Henry is my darling Jack Russell Terrier he's been with me for years. He's very old now and he accompanies me everywhere. The tourists on the schooners love him; he's absolutely great with children." Maria smiled and her thoughts turned to far off Margate. She wondered how Poppy and her faithful little dog, Jack the Lad, were coping without her. "Henry is welcome here! Prepare to start 7 am sharp on Monday morning and bring a basket or little bed for Henry. We can't have him in the kitchen but he can hang out on the porch or in the sewing room. I pay well for the right people. We'll discuss the chocolate cake recipe on Monday and how we'll make a success of our little café and soup kitchen."

Monday came around quickly and Ruth, punctual as always, duly arrived on the doorstep just as the antique grandfather clock in the spacious hall chimed seven o'clock. When Maria opened the door a spunky Jack Russell Terrier greeted her. Henry had been to the groomers over the weekend and sported a cute navy-blue printed bandanna decorated with tiny white sailing ships. A beaming Ruth said, "Henry immediately captures everyone's heart, he's so friendly and puts even the most sensitive of people at ease." Maria bent down to stroke his glistening white and brown coat and whispered, "Henry will be a great gift to this special place. I'm glad that you brought him along." They sat down in the large dining room and over coffee and freshly baked croissants they began to talk at length about Maria's vision.

"Ruth, we open our doors on September 20th that's the feast day of St. Eustace. I've ordered some elegant wicker furniture for this very large dining room and for outside on the wrap around porch. It should arrive in a few days. There's room for four round tables here in the dining room, four chairs to each table. Six round tables will fit outside on the porch. I want pastel blue linen tablecloths on each table and there'll be matching napkins. Six navy blue wingback armchairs are also coming soon. Maria pointed to a large recessed area with window seats overlooking the wrap around porch. In that area we'll place the armchairs and two coffee tables. That area will be for informal gatherings as people come in for morning coffee or a cup of tea."

Ruth looked around the beautiful room. The floor was made of narrow polished oak boards. There were three high ceiling fans and lovely stained-glass windows overlooking the wrap around porch. As the early morning sunlight filtered through the stained glass it threw magical rainbow beams of light onto the walls. The recessed window seats were covered with bright yellow and blue printed seat cushions along with smaller scatter ones. The walls were painted pastel blue and there were many large but tasteful oil and acrylic paintings of tropical scenery and seascapes. Everything was so fresh and colourful. Comfortable and elegant yet very welcoming seemed to sum it all up. Maria could sense Ruth's curiosity and she began to share Dick and Dolly's story, the sad demise of their beloved David and their focus in later years directed towards creating a place of healing, reflection and remembrance to celebrate the life of their only child.

Maria began to discuss the practicalities of running the kitchen and she introduced Ruth to her very special Sachertorte chocolate cake recipe. "Ruth this is a famous classic Viennese cake. It consists of flourless chocolate sponge cake cut into three layers, between which apricot jam is thickly spread and it's covered with rich frosting. I use grated nuts instead of flour and only the very best organic, fair-trade dark chocolate. Chocolate is very important it's a great healer. It helps people to feel good, connect with one another and warms the heart. Homemade Sachertorte will be an important offering here at St. Eustace so before we officially open you need to get in some practice and perfect your baking!" Ruth sat back and smiled. Working with Maria Popoff was going to be quite the adventure and a challenge. She began to wonder exactly what she might have let herself in for. A sudden sharp rap at the oak front door broke the silence and startled both women. Maria rose and went to see who was there.

Cora had noticed Maria's advert in a local magazine a few days previously and today she'd plucked up enough courage to leave home and walk the short distance to St. Eustace. She was not a well woman. Cora was extremely highly strung and at the end of her tether. She was worn down by unhappiness and continual vigilance. Today she felt some unseen force literally push her out of her home and propel her down the street. Cora's husband was a successful businessman who spent much of his time either at his Key West office or travelling. In their home he'd become conspicuous by his absence. They lived in the well to do part of town in a pleasant house set amongst a well-kept tropical garden. Cora was indeed blessed with a lovely home and plenty of money to purchase whatever she needed but she was terribly lonely and always felt like a prisoner. She longed to join her friends from her younger days and socialize but they'd turned their back on her years ago. She had no support and her husband had mostly run away. Then there was their Linda.

Cora felt that her only child had become a ball and chain around her neck. Linda first began to display problems when she was two years old. She would scream endlessly and nothing seemed to quiet her distress. The screaming improved as she grew older but she never learnt to speak not even one word. Linda wandered continuously around the house touching things, tidying up and carefully placing things in long lines. Initially friends encouraged Cora and her husband to take Linda to a number of specialist doctors. They didn't want to accept that their child was different and acknowledge that there was something wrong, abnormal even. The autistic diagnosis, when she was five years old, came as a big blow. Linda's father pushed it under the carpet and hid away in his office telling Cora to deal with it. Tragically Linda became the bane of Cora's life. No matter how she tried to love her child life was so very difficult. Linda attended a number of schools but there always came a time when the school would call Cora and asked her to take Linda home because they couldn't cope with her weird behaviour, lack of language and her terrible tantrums. Cora tried to home school her but it was all so fruitless. Linda never learnt to speak or to read. All she wanted to do all day long was to touch things and tidy up. Cora couldn't take her out and about because she caused so much embarrassment and chaos in the shops and restaurants. Both mother and daughter had become prisoners in their lovely home. Today was different. Cora's weekly cleaner arrived early and on the spur of the moment she asked if she would keep a watchful eye on Linda, lock all the doors and pocket the keys because something urgent had come up.

As soon as Maria caught sight of the anguished Cora standing so forlornly on the doorstep of St. Eustace, she sensed immediately the urgency of the situation and knew in her heart that GRACE had truly intervened that day. Cora was invited to join Maria and Ruth in the dining room and over a cup of coffee and a slice of Maria's divine chocolate cake she was invited to share her story. Towards the end of her tale of woe Cora sat back weeping and whispered between her sobs, "If something doesn't change in the next few weeks, I'm going to take my own life because I just can't cope any longer. I don't see a future, my life is joyless, I feel that I'm in a deep black hole and just can't see a way out." Ruth cast a glance at Maria expressing her alarm.

Maria gently reached for Cora's frail hands and clutching them both tightly and looking into her eyes she said, "Cora there's always hope and a better way. You and Linda will find healing here at St. Eustace. Tell me, if we employ your Linda, what gift will she bring to St. Eustace? We all have gifts. Think hard and tell us what she's good at."

Cora dried her eyes and looked up, "Are you serious? This is the first time anyone has ever extended a helping hand to me. Linda understands everything but she's never said a word. I believe that she's really quite clever. She's very tidy in fact it's an absolute obsession. She loves to be in the kitchen and will stand at the kitchen sink for hours washing up; carefully drying the dishes and arranging everything neatly in the cupboards. Things have to be perfect. She also loves to clean. Dusting and polishing are favourite pastimes and if she gets hold of scissors, she cuts things up. In truth she can't sit still. Her hands always want to be busy. If she can't be busy, she becomes very bad tempered but her screaming and yelling have improved now that she's older. She just celebrated her 19th birthday."

Maria smiled, "Cora, there's plenty here to occupy Linda's busy hands. We'll be serving morning coffee and afternoon tea on fine bone china edged with gold. This china is not suitable for a dishwasher. Linda can hand wash and dry the dishes, put them away and she can help Ruth to clear away the tables, wash them down and lay new table cloths as the customers come and go. She can load the washing machine and do the ironing. Is she capable of this type of work?" Cora had dried her eyes and was looking so much more positive. "Yes, as long as no one expects her to talk she'll do an amazing job for you. The dishes will be spotless, the kitchen cupboards will be tidier than you could ever have imagined and she's great at ironing too." Maria laughed, "Cora, then it's all settled! Linda can start on Monday next week. You can come along for a few days to help her get started. Harriet and Bella will be settled in the sewing room by then. They'll be making frocks from the 1940's - 1960's era so I think Linda could help them out too. If she's handy with a pair of scissors the two sisters can teach her how to lay patterns on the material and cut it out. This will keep her busy hands more than occupied and who knows in time and with love and support from the St. Eustace caring community she might just speak one day! We won't have Ruth to work the café at the weekends so perhaps you would consider joining us then and helping out. Ruth will do all the necessary baking during the week so it would just mean serving tea and coffee, pastries, scones and cake. Do you think you can do that in return for us taking your Linda under our wing?" Cora smiled and said, "Of course, I would love to be part of your community and having five days to myself I can gather my strength, heal my jangled nerves and I'll be better able to take on life's challenges."

Cora left St. Eustace with a spring in her step because for the first time in such a very long time she began to see that there just might be light at the end of the dark tunnel. Her life had become her prison, today she'd found hope. Maria and Ruth continued to discuss the practicalities of managing the café and soup kitchen. Ruth recalled that Betty, one of the girls working on the schooners, was always looking for extra money. "She's a student participating in a distance learning program. I know she's hard working, reliable and popular with the tourists. I could ask if she would be interested in coming in during the week perhaps for a couple of hours to help me prepare vegetables for home-made soup and to bake bread rolls." Maria smiled; it really did feel as if everything was coming together. She showed Ruth around the very well-equipped kitchen. Together they opened the cupboards and examined the beautiful bone china that Dolly had collected over her lifetime. It had become an all-consuming hobby especially after she'd lost her David. Dolly would frequent all the local antique shops and attend estate sales and over time she amassed a fine collection of beautiful china. Teapots with matching cups and saucers and dainty plates had always been her favourite.

With the café side of business nicely taking shape Maria begun to direct her attention towards the vintage emporium. She'd always tapped into her many worldwide sources to stock her shops. Now it was time to get busy. Poppy would often wonder where on earth some of her merchandise had actually come from. Maria, mysterious as ever, vanished for several days on one of these hunting expeditions. During that time Ruth began to familiarize herself with the kitchen and began to tackle the chocolate cake and scone recipes that Maria had asked her to master. Harriet and Bella arrived early on Tuesday morning and established themselves in the sewing room. While busily working away on their old sewing machines they began to enjoy the tempting smells coming from the kitchen and the opportunity to sample the fruits of Ruth's labour. By Friday afternoon the two elderly sisters had invited their Bible study women's group to gather around the large table in the sewing room for prayers, tea and chocolate cake. Bella told them that Ruth needed some guinea pigs to sample her baking. The church ladies enjoyed themselves so much that they asked if this could become a regular calendar event!

Maria's return to St. Eustace on Saturday in a large rental truck packed full of vintage paraphernalia coincided with a visit from Desmond. The tall flamboyantly dressed young man in his early 30's arrived on the doorstep around noon. The house was unusually quiet. Ruth was away working on the schooners. Pastor Joe had collected Bella and Harriet in the battered old yellow school bus and was taking them off on a church luncheon outing. Cousin Rollo was out in the garages tinkering and Maria was sitting in the kitchen sipping a cup of tea and wondering who she could summon to help her unload and where exactly would she display everything.

The loud urgent rap disturbing the quietness of St. Eustace brought a startled Maria to her feet. She waddled hurriedly towards the large oak front door. A beaming Desmond announced himself and said, "I'm so glad to see someone is here. It's all so quiet! I saw your advert a few days ago calling for special people so I thought that I would come and enquire. I'm curious and very game to explore mysterious ads. One never knows what one is letting oneself in for!" Maria smiled she liked the look of this jolly, inquisitive young man. "Cross my threshold and we'll have some tea and a slice of my special chocolate cake and get to know each other." Once settled in the kitchen with a cup of tea in his hand Desmond began to tell his story.

He was an out of work artist and could easily turn his hand to anything of an artistic nature. "I grew up in New York, went to college to study speech and drama and fine art. For several years I worked on Broadway. I had some small stage parts but in more recent years I've been designing and making glamorous costumes for some of the big shows. Unfortunately, due to this terrible Covid mess I lost my job. The theatres shut down along with my livelihood so I made my way to Key West. There didn't seem much point staying around in New York. Rent for my small flat went through the roof, cold weather and being stuck inside a tiny box didn't excite me at all. Friends in the Key West gay community encouraged me to come to the sun and fun. I arrived earlier this year but still can't find an enjoyable job. I've waited tables in a number of local bars and restaurants. I've also done a few gardening jobs but sadly I just haven't found anything that makes my heart sing and is rewarding enough for me to get up each morning with a spring in my step."

Maria smiled because deep in her heart she felt that her prayers had been answered. Desmond would be a good fit in their eclectic little community. Before she could speak, he suddenly said, "I'm really hoping that you are accepting of a gay employee. When I finally plucked up the courage to come clean with my parents and siblings about my sexuality, they threw me out and told me in no uncertain terms that they never wanted to see or hear from me again. It took me years to deal with my abandonment issues. I went through a lot of counselling but even today my heart still aches and yearns to be back in the fold." Maria gently took his hands and looking deep into his eyes she said, "Desmond come and join us here at St. Eustace you'll find healing here together with a sense of belonging and purpose. We don't discriminate. Everyone is welcome here and encouraged to share their own special gifts in our all-inclusive community."

Desmond breathed a sigh of relief. "Thank you it has been so very hard for me. I just knew when I saw your advert that I should come and see for myself this place called St. Eustace. It's funny I could almost feel some unseen force pushing me down the road!" Maria laughed, "Yes, those who need to be here will eventually find their way to my doorstep. Welcome! There's much to do. I'm wondering if you have time to begin this new chapter of your life right now?" Looking somewhat surprised Desmond agreed and a relieved Maria took him outside to survey the large hire truck in the driveway packed full of merchandise.

Desmond was a gem. Being so strong and sturdy he made light work of unloading the merchandise. By the end of the day all the large boxes were stacked neatly in the hallway and in the spacious large dining room. The new wicker furniture had yet to arrive so there was plenty of room. Exhausted and thirsty Maria invited him to come and sit in the kitchen and enjoy a glass of ice-cold lemonade and a plate of her freshly baked fruit scones. Cousin Rollo joined them and they shared the history of St. Eustace. They told Desmond all about Dick, Dolly and the loss of their cherished son, David. Maria went on to talk about Bella and Harriet's arrival and the creation of a sewing room followed by Ruth, Cora and Linda and the plans for a café and a soup kitchen. "We are a growing community. Cousin Rollo has plans for the garages and workshops but we are working to a deadline. September 20th is the feast of St. Eustace so there's still much to be done. Desmond, can you work six days a week until we get established?" Desmond nodded he already felt part of the big picture. "I'll come bright and early tomorrow and we can talk about how you want your vintage store set up. I'm not sure if this is of interest but I do know that there's an old clothing store out on the highway just as you leave town. The owners placed an advert in the same paper where I noticed yours. They are closing up due to retirement and have an estate sale tomorrow at 11am. Perhaps we might find shelving and racks to hold and display the merchandise and maybe pick up other useful bits and pieces?" Maria smiled, "Desmond what a good idea. You and I can meet here at 8am and take a look at the rooms in St. Eustace where I would like to set up my shop. Then we can take the hire van over to the estate sale and hopefully we'll find some display items that will help us to get sorted and create my emporium."

Desmond was as good as his word. He appeared bright and punctual on Sunday morning. Together they looked over the very large sitting room cum artistic studio that Dolly had set up in her lifetime. The area was situated off to the left-hand side of St. Eustace as one entered the oak front door and could be accessed by large double doors from the spacious entrance hall. It really was an ideal area to set up shop. Dolly had replaced the old oak flooring with the most beautiful porcelain tiles. They were a lovely Italian geometric design. The tiles were richly glazed with iridescent blue, white and yellow. The walls were painted a pastel lemon and there was a fine light oak wainscot decorating the lower four feet of the walls. Beautiful stained glass windows depicting woodland scenes looked onto the wrap around porch at the front and sides of the home. Thankfully Desmond and Maria had been left with a blank canvas to work with because Cousin Rollo had cleared the area away after taking possession of the home. The furniture wasn't to his taste. He moved all of Dolly's art supplies and easels into the garage and workshop area and he'd donated the hundreds of books that filled two large oak bookcases to a local second-hand bookshop. "Those bookcases, with their deep sleeves, will come in very handy for the store," remarked Maria as she and Desmond headed off out of town towards the estate sale in the hire truck.

Few people had gathered outside the doors of the old clothing store in anticipation of the 11am opening. The store was a treasured family business spanning many generations. It was extremely old fashioned, antiquated even. Maria's beady eyes immediately settled upon three ancient glass display counter tops with beautifully carved wooden drawers underneath. Desmond spotted more modern looking clothing display racks suitable for their large inventory of frocks. Maria noticed several mannequins suitable to display costumes and there were a number of mannequin heads ideal for displaying hats. They also noticed several beautifully carved oak tables that would be perfect for displaying merchandise and there were a number of ancient looking shoe racks too. The elderly proprietors were delighted that such a large number of their estate sale display fixtures and fittings were going intact to one particular person.

George and Connie had run their little business for over 50 years and before that the store belonged to Connie's parents and their parents before them. "Sadly, we're just too old and frail these days and we just can't keep going. We really do need to retire and rest up. We're both drained of energy and this Corona virus crisis hasn't helped at all. Life has become difficult and we no longer have any strength left for our treasured business. Unfortunately, there are no relatives or friends able and willing to continue in our shoes," lamented Connie. Maria, noticing tears in her eyes, gently took her hand and said, "Connie we shall absolutely treasure your fixtures and fittings. These ancient countertops and tables have many stories to tell and we'll honour and respect their history. They'll find a new home at St. Eustace and we'll love, care and appreciate them as much as you, George, your parents and grandparents before you always have done."

Connie dried her eyes and looked Maria in the eye. Puzzled she whispered to herself, "How on earth does this wizened old woman know the secrets of my heart? How does she understand the distress of having to close our doors? How does she know the pain of having to let go of so many treasures? How does she know how painful it was to put that CLOSED sign in the window after offering such a fine, reputable service to the Key West community for generations?" Maria held her hand tightly and simply said, "I'll do my best to love your treasures they're all special. Connie please do bring George and stop by St. Eustace in a few days' time and see them safely in their new home. I'll have a little bottle of *Walnut* waiting for you. This flower essence helps ease the passage of change. It will help you and George to let go and settle into this next chapter of your life."

George had engaged a few local lads to help those who'd purchased large items at their estate sale to load up their cars, vans and trucks. Desmond and Maria were glad of the extra help and two of the lads agreed to ride along in the truck back to St. Eustace to help Desmond unload and place the newly acquired treasures inside. Cousin Rollo appeared from the garages and lent a hand too and when all was complete Maria treated everyone to ice-cold lemonade and freshly baked scones in the kitchen.

A New Beginning:

St. Eustace - Back of House

Rollo loved to potter around in the workshops and garages at the rear of St. Eustace. They were all in an excellent state of repair. Dick and Dolly had spent as much time and care on these important buildings as St. Eustace itself. There were four red brick garages and three of them housed Dick's collection of vintage classic cars. There was a 1930 Cadillac 16, a 1932 Pontiac Roadster and a Ford Model T. The cars had waited patiently for Dick's undivided attention but unfortunately that time never came. Dick's energy and focus was always somewhere else so they continued to gather dust during his lifetime. Cousin Rollo had great plans. He envisioned a sort of *shed experience* providing an opportunity for men to gather sharing skills and camaraderie without all the alcohol and smoky atmospheres that the bars and public houses offered. The fourth garage was particularly large and well equipped with all kinds of mechanical equipment. There were several large workbenches and many racks crammed full of tools, nuts, bolts, and screws etc.

In addition to the four garages there was a long single story brick building housing all Dick's gold and silversmith tools and equipment. Four large ceiling fans kept the whitewashed work area cool and several large picture windows provided extra light. One of the windows was round and had a beautiful countryside scene fashioned out of stained glass. At one end of this building was a comfortable room used as an office space and equipped with a single kitchen unit housing a double burner stove, a small fridge and a kitchen sink. In the entrance lobby by the main access door there was a room off to the right that housed a toilet and washbasin and another larger room to the left that housed a bath, shower, basin and toilet.

In preparation for the September 20th grand opening Cousin Rollo placed an advertisement in a number of local papers and journals.

Announcing a special community spirited gathering place for men. Come share your skills in our garages and workshops. Learn new things, develop friendships and become a part of the St. Eustace caring community.

Callers always welcome at St. Eustace, ask to speak with Rollo

Over the next few weeks Madam Popoff, Desmond, Ruth, Betty, Cora, Linda, Bella and Harriet all settled into a St. Eustace routine. They busily prepared for the grand opening on September 20th. During that time a number of men appeared at the front door asking for Cousin Rollo. They were directed to the back yard and so it was that a motley crew of interesting folk of all shapes, sizes, ethnicity and remarkable talents were quickly assembled. It was during this time that Fred also showed up. He was painfully thin, shabbily dressed with long straggly hair and a beard to match. Cousin Rollo recalled the day very clearly. It was wet and windy. The garages and workshops were deserted. Cousin Rollo was busily preoccupied sorting through boxes of screws and washers. Fred stood at the door to the long brick workshop building dripping pools of water and shivering. Cousin Rollo quickly beckoned for him to cross the threshold, remove his sodden canvas shoes and his shirt and sit down on the wooden picnic bench by the door. He scurried away to the back-office area and quickly reappeared with an old tartan blanket, a mug of steaming hot tea and a slice of Maria's divine chocolate cake. Cousin Rollo sensed immediately that Fred would require a great deal of help and loving care. As Fred sipped his tea, he told his story.

"I grew up in the Midwest. My family was particularly well known in the small town. We lived in a large house. Father was a successful businessman and my mother was a socialite. They had extremely high expectations for their only son. There was always far too much pressure. I was expected to perform like a circus animal! Do this, do that, say this, say that, don't go there and wear this outfit. It was all so sickening. In the end I felt that I just couldn't breathe. I could never be my own person. My life was all planned out, the school I had to attend, the university to follow, the occupation that I was expected to pursue and even the friends that I was allowed to mingle with. I was even told the sports and musical instruments that I was expected to play. Eventually, towards the end of my third year at university, I suffered a nervous breakdown. One day I just got up and walked away. I disappeared into thin air. I never told anyone what I was doing or where I was going.

I hitch hiked down to Florida. I was fed up with Midwest winters where there's snow on the ground for almost five months every year. I just knew that I had to find the sun. I've been here in Key West for several years now. I ran away to the end of the country needing to escape. I wanted to be as far away as possible. It hasn't been easy because I got myself mixed up with the wrong crowd. They introduced me to the drug scene. It seemed like a good way to escape but these days I'm not so sure. I didn't like what the drugs were doing to my mind and to my body. It took a lot to eventually get me to kick the habit. I had a girlfriend called Fiona, she really cared about me and helped me then one day I discovered her limp body. I was so shocked, she was dead; apparently, she'd overdosed after a bad argument with the owner of the café where she worked as a cook. After Fiona's death I took a deep dive into a black sea of depression. I was caught up in dark night of the soul stuff. I questioned who I was, why I was still here, what was my purpose and why I'd become a tramp sleeping rough on the beach or in shop doorways. Yesterday something strange happened. I woke up and someone had left a magazine by my sleeping bag. When I saw your advert asking for help at St. Eustace, I just felt deep down in the very depths of my being that I needed to come and introduce myself. It was as if some unseen force was pushing me to come here."

Cousin Rollo sat back, took a long deep breath and reached his hands out towards Fred. "You're most welcome here at St. Eustace. We'll provide you with a proper home in return for help. We could do with someone to tend to the large gardens and mow the lawns. We need someone on hand that can act as a caretaker to keep an eye out at night and make sure that the house and garages are secure as the evening draws to a close. My elderly cousin, Maria, will be the only person staying upstairs in the grand house. We've a back office here in this building. It has a small kitchen unit; there's a bathroom and I can have a single bed brought in with some other furniture so that you have a proper home to call your very own."

Fred couldn't believe his luck. For the past three years he'd made his bed on the beach or in a doorway. When the weather had been really bad be joined the queues seeking shelter at the local Salvation Army hostel for the homeless. There were many young and old people just like himself. All had run away to the end of the highway. He'd worked a number of different jobs over the years. At first, when he looked more respectable, he had waited tables in tourist cafes but lately he was lucky if he could find the odd job tending someone's garden or helping out on a building site.

Cousin Rollo looked Fred directly in the eye and said, "I've a good feeling about you Fred. Don't ever let me down. I trust that you will always act and work with honesty, integrity and responsibility. I'm giving you a chance to get your feet back on the ground and to grow into your own person with respect and dignity. I'm offering you a comfortable bed, a roof over your head and a proper bathroom all of your own. I only have one special request and it's a sort of contract and condition of your employment here at St. Eustace. You tell me that several years ago you simply disappeared into thin air. You turned your back on your parents and upon your wider family and friends. No matter what has happened between you and your parents in the past it is now time for you to tell them that you are safe and gainfully employed. That's all that I ask and in your own time, but that is a promise that I expect you to keep. Go away and think about the time that we've spent together today. Consider my contract. If you feel able and willing to follow through then bid your street friends goodbye and come tomorrow morning bright and early with your belongings ready to begin a new chapter of your life. I'll wait for you until noon tomorrow and then that door of opportunity will close."

Fred looked wistfully out of the window. The rain had stopped and the sun was shining through the beautiful stained-glass window. It cast rainbow shards of light onto the whitewashed wall. St. Eustace felt like a good place, a safe place. Rollo seemed like a very special old man but he drove a hard bargain. He'd always vowed that he would never speak to his parents again. He blamed them for so many unhappy things in his disturbed past. He didn't know if he would even be able to let go of the resentment and finally reach out with an olive branch. With hunched shoulders he stood up and said, "Thank you Rollo for your time, the tea and cake and for your very generous offer. I'll give it careful thought. However, it's a very tall order."

Fred slipped on his sodden canvas shoes and shirt. The rain had stopped and he stepped out into the sunshine. Rollo sighed and wished with all of his heart that Fred would ultimately choose the wisest path. Returning to his patch on a dirty, derelict piece of scrubland bordering the beach on the edge of town he cast his eyes down upon his handful of comrades. They were all in the same boat, lonely and bearing deep-seated mental and emotional scars. Fred acknowledged that he was the only sober one amongst them. Most of them stumbled from one alcoholic or drug induced coma to another. This was the sum of their days and long nights. Fred shrugged his shoulders and sighed. Deep down he knew that he wanted more from his dismal life but taking the bold step of contacting his parents was both scary and overwhelming. He clambered into the warmth of his sleeping bag. The sun was sinking low over the horizon. Flocks of snowy white egrets were flying overhead to their roosting grounds. Lovers were walking hand in hand by the water's edge and heading for home or to their comfy hotel.

That night his sleep was disturbed by a strange dream in fact he couldn't decide if he was actually dreaming or if this really happened. An old wizened woman appeared; she came from the sea in an ancient clinker-built rowboat. As the boat approached the shallow water she scrambled ashore with great difficulty and pulled the boat up onto the sand. She shook him and began to talk in urgent tones. An almost full moon lighted up her wrinkled old face. Her piercing all seeing eyes shook him to the very core.

"Fred, pick yourself up. The clocks on earth are ticking and it's time for you to act. Make something of your life. Examine your heart and find the courage to let your parents know that at least you are alive and well. In time, when you are stronger, make an effort to mend your broken pieces. You have many gifts and talents; some are yet to be discovered. Look around you. A path from this living hell has been cleared for you and now it's up to you to find the courage and walk those first few steps. It's not going to be easy but there'll always be a brighter tomorrow to look forward to."

The old woman disappeared as suddenly as she came. This time a young girl joined her in the ancient rowing boat. Her face was pale; she had long blonde hair and she wore a gypsy skirt. When she turned around Fred recognized her face, it was his Fiona. She smiled and blew him a kiss as the boat disappeared over the horizon. The next morning, he woke early to the calling of noisy seagulls. He gathered together his sleeping bag and tattered rucksack and he hastily scribbled a note leaving it beside his good friend Charlie.

I've finally found some courage. I'm heading off to a better place. Sending good vibes to you all for a different tomorrow. God bless.
Your friend,
Fred.

Cousin Rollo arrived bright and early at St. Eustace. He'd mixed feelings today. He hoped that with all his heart that Fred would show up. Over his many years as a healer Rollo knew it was so very hard for the homeless folk to get back on their feet and take their first steps towards a better future. In his experience they were all so unpredictable. Their hurts ran deep and sometimes it proved impossible to make a difference. Sadly, he'd known far too many cases of suicide. He was enjoying a pot of coffee and a plate of freshly baked croissants with Maria on the front porch when a lonely figure struggled up the driveway carrying a rolled up sleeping bag and a tattered rucksack. The elderly couple turned and smiled at each other and under her breath Maria muttered to herself, "mission accomplished!"

An excited and thankful Rollo invited Fred to join them on the porch for breakfast. Ruth appeared with another pot of coffee, an extra mug and another plate of croissants. They spent the best part of an hour discussing his future employment at St. Eustace. It was September 18th and only two days away from the grand opening. When Harriet and Bella arrived, Maria requested that they put their frock making on hold and made some colourful cotton shirts for Fred. They'd recently acquired several bolts of fabric sporting beautiful tropical botanical prints. After taking his measurements the two ladies set to work making him several short and long-sleeved shirts. Rollo took Fred down the road to the local barber so that his long greasy, straggly hair could be thoroughly washed and trimmed. The barber trimmed his beard too. The wash and brush up was immediately transformative. The next stop was the local men's clothing store where Rollo purchased a pile of shorts and long trousers for Fred together with suitable underwear and several pairs of new shoes.

They made their way back to St. Eustace where arrangements were made for a local furniture store to deliver a brand-new single bed and mattress later that day to the workshop office area. Ruth found time to go upstairs in the grand house and search through the linen cupboards. She found sheets, pillows and a light duvet together with a stack of bath towels, washcloths and bath rugs. Soap, toothpaste and shampoo were added to her bags. She delivered her finds to the office area where Fred would take up residence. Later she rifled through the kitchen cabinets and found him a supply of saucepans, cutlery and crockery so that he could prepare his own evening meal.

By the end of the day Fred was in a daze. It had been such a whirlwind of drama. By the time he finished soaking in a long hot bath and donned his new clothes he looked in the mirror and saw a transformed man beyond recognition. Upon reflection he couldn't help but feel that he somehow recognized Rollo's cousin. She seemed so familiar. It was many weeks later when he was firmly established in the St. Eustace household and he'd finally found the courage to write a short note and mail it to his parents that he put the pieces together. One night while he lay in bed thinking about his new life, he muttered to himself, "She's the old woman who came in from the sea with Fiona! She told me that the clocks on earth were ticking and to make something of my life!"

September 19th was an extremely busy day for the St. Eustace community as they made the house and workshops ready for the grand opening. Ruth was busy in the kitchen baking chocolate cake and fruit scones. Cora had come in to help out and Linda was enjoying every minute of her new life. Today she threw herself into passionately polishing; dusting and tidying everything she could possibly lay her hands upon. Harriet and Bella, over the past few weeks, had made over 50 beautiful 1950's hip-hop skirts and dresses between them. Today they were enjoying setting them out on the new shop fixtures and fittings that Desmond and Maria had recently purchased at the estate sale. They loved dressing the mannequins and artistically creating a lovely display of their handiwork in the large hallway.

Desmond had been out in the gardens picking large bunches of colourful tropical flowers and foliage and was creating beautiful arrangements for the dining room, the hall and the shop. He'd recently discovered a large collection of tall elegant vases perfect for his handiwork. Dolly had acquired these over the years and stored them all away in the attic room of the brick turret. They'd remained hidden and forgotten until Desmond had ventured up there when he first explored the grand house.

Maria and Cousin Rollo busied themselves arranging strings of colourful bunting made by Harriet and Bella. They hung it up on the wrought iron railings along with a large banner that a local printer had created for them.

Welcome to St. Eustace we are finally opening on September 20ᵗʰ at 2pm!

The elderly couple smiled as they stood back and admired their handiwork. Cousin Rollo put his arm around Maria and chuckled, "Maria, we've actually made it all happen! St. Eustace has come to life. Of course, the real work is only just beginning. However, we already have and will continue to make a difference in the lives of so many who've crossed our threshold. Then there are those who've yet to come to this very special place. St. Eustace awaits their arrival too!" Maria smiled. It had been such very hard work. She was old and tired yet there was still much more work to be done. Her mind wandered back to Margate and the Isle of Thanet. She quietly reflected upon the three vintage shops left in Poppy's capable hands. There hadn't been much time to reflect and to miss her past life in all the drama of the past few weeks. Maria felt that all of the troubled souls who'd recently made their way to Dick and Dolly's legacy had helped to keep her spirits and her energy fuelled up.

The feast day of St. Eustace was a tremendous success. Although September 20ᵗʰ was a Monday crowds came and gathered by the gate just before 2pm. Local people were particularly curious. They'd heard about a strange old woman who'd joined old Rollo. They'd heard about her delicious chocolate cake and freshly baked scones. They heard about the vintage boutique and the garage/workshop project. They were curious and wanted to know more. The tourists came because free cake and tea were on offer today and they'd heard that there was to be a concert in the gardens during the late afternoon and early evening. Folding chairs had been borrowed from a local hotel specializing in destination weddings. Cousin Rollo knew the manager. Over the years they'd become good friends. He kindly offered the chairs and makeshift stage free of charge for the opening event.

When plans were initially drawn up for the grand opening Harriet and Bella talked with Pastor Joe. The Baptist Church Spiritualist Choir offered to do a 30-minute concert and had been practicing for several weeks. Cousin Rollo was extremely well connected around Key West; he knew all kinds of townsfolk. He'd helped many of them return to better health so when word got out that musicians were required for the grand opening concert program many volunteered their services. The large crowd, sitting on wedding chairs or rugs brought from home, enjoyed the three-hour program. The front lawns were a mass of happy folk loving the vast selection of musical talents. As the sun went down a myriad of fairy lights lit up the gardens and the house. It was one of those magical evenings when one felt good to be alive. Troubles were forgotten. People were happy and gave freely when three top hats were passed around to collect money for various local charities.

When the gates were finally closed at 10pm Maria and Rollo congratulated their special band of helpers. They hugged them all and Rollo gave a little speech.

> *"St. Eustace has made its mark upon our community at the end of the highway. This is the beginning of many adventures. We're all travellers helping one another and reaching out to our neighbours. Together we'll make a difference. We'll help create a better world right here on our own doorstep. Thank you."*

Much to everyone's amazement and delight Cora's Linda spoke her first words ever:

> *"Yes, we're all travellers!"*

Margate Calls

Maria's sleep was restless that night. Once everyone had gone home, she wearily climbed the stairs to her bedroom and feeling totally exhausted she quickly fell into bed. However, in her dreams Poppy was calling for her and Maria had always promised that she would return if ever the need should arise. That night Maria felt herself being drawn back across the vast Atlantic Ocean to the tiny corner of East Kent that she'd grown to love so much. The local area was currently enjoying an Indian summer. It was September 21st, *World Peace Day*, and Maria found herself walking along the deserted sands by the Nayland Rock just as the sun was rising in the east. As she neared the harbour she noticed a few additional boats, certainly more than she remembered. There was a sunken fishing boat over by the harbour arm near Mala Kaffe. Anchored just off the slipway from Manning's Seafood Shack was a sailing yacht resting in the mud on her bilge keels with the intriguing name, SEA TARDIS. Maria headed over to her shop on King Street. It was still very early. She slipped into the back room and made herself a cup of coffee and waited patiently for Poppy and Gertrude to arrive.

Poppy arrived first. She was pale and looked particularly flustered. As Jack the Lad ran to greet her Poppy breathed a sigh of relief. "I'm so happy to see you. I've been praying that you would come and visit. It's been such a difficult week! One of those times when absolutely nothing has gone right. For a start all of the clocks in the shop have stopped at three o'clock. A number of our customers have fallen over the doorstep and several have been particularly obnoxious, demanding and extremely irritable. The lights have flickered in the late afternoon as we've prepared to shut up for the day. This all began when I found a bundle of old clothes left on the doorstep. There really wasn't anything worth salvaging or suitable for sale in the shop. The clothes were particularly old and moth eaten, men's clothes, presumably hidden away in someone's attic or basement. I threw them all away except one item. I found a very antiquated looking life vest; it was better preserved compared to the rest of the bundle. It had been carefully wrapped in faded tissue paper, then in strong brown paper tied with string and placed in an old canvas sail bag. I'm just wondering now if it is this lifejacket that has brought with it some kind of troubled energy, an ill wind if you like, into our shop. It has certainly disturbed the peace. We're all at sea right now, quite literally!"

Maria Popoff sensed immediately the painful vibrations emanating from the old life vest and asked several questions. "Poppy dear, have you held it? Have you discovered its story? Remember, I've taught you many times in the past that belongings have energy to share. Sometimes it's a good energy, sometimes bad and sometimes it's downright evil! Possessions can reflect the lives of their owners. What have you discovered about this old life vest?" Poppy looked sheepish. "To be honest I was immediately afraid of this old life vest. Somehow, I knew deep inside that I should not get involved with its story. However, on the other hand, I felt that it was wrong to just cast it away with the other things in the bundle. I feel that this old life vest may have a message for us but I'm not quite sure what that message might be. It's all a bit of a mystery but my sixth sense told me to leave well alone and to call you in because this life vest requires some expert handling."

Maria stood up and smiled. She felt so very proud and delighted with Poppy's continued growth in all things of a spiritual nature. "Yes, indeed so, Poppy. This life vest has a story and a lesson for all of us to acknowledge and to embrace." She took the old life vest; disappeared into the back room with Jack the Lad following closely at her heels and having shut the door she sank into one of the comfy armchairs. Maria clutched the life vest to her heart and its story began to unfold.

It was 1885 when Juliana and Benigno left the poverty of a far-flung remote village in southern Italy. Benigno had too many able-bodied brothers and there was no work to support him on the family farm. The young couple were recently married and eager to seek out a better life. They'd little in the way of money and few possessions. Eventually they ended up in Paris where Juliana helped to clean a large hotel in the city centre and where Benigno worked in the kitchens. When their only child, Alessandro, was born in the summer of 1887 they decided to move on. Benigno heard that many Italian families, all in search of a better life, had settled across the English Channel in East Kent. During the nineteenth century and earlier Britain had an open-door policy towards immigration. It was not until 1905 that any controls were put in place to limit the entry of immigrants into Britain.

The young couple and baby Alessandro settled in Margate and for a number of years Benigno worked several menial jobs. Luckily, he could turn his hand to most things. Eventually he went to work for the Morelli family in neighbouring Broadstairs. This family established a successful ice cream business, initially operating from a bicycle down by the seafront. Eventually they made it to the big time and even supplied Harrods Food Hall in London. Juliana, Benigno and Alessandro enjoyed the bracing, clean sea air and the lovely beaches that the local area had to offer. On Sundays they took Alessandro to play on the beach and paddle in the sea but he never learnt to swim. He was always particularly frightened of the deep murky water. As the hardworking Benigno became more successful in business the family were able to improve their standard of living, they eventually purchased a small terraced home on Milton Avenue in Margate.

Alessandro grew up strong and healthy. In 1901 at the age of 14 he took up an apprenticeship with a local firm of carpenters and eventually became a very skilled and popular tradesman. When he was 20 years old, he met Rosa who became the love of his life. She was four years younger and the daughter of another Italian family who'd emigrated from Italy at the turn of the century. They met at a local dance and stepped out for the best part of two years before they planned their wedding to coincide with her eighteenth birthday in 1909. However, their plans were abruptly curtailed when Rosa's family received the news that they'd inherited the large family farm back in their home country. Relatives were urging them to return. Sadly, Rosa's parents had never taken a liking to Alessandro. They always felt that their beautiful and talented daughter could do much better in marriage. They were reluctant to leave her behind and she was under considerable pressure to return with them. The young couple were heartbroken as they bade their farewells. They agreed to write and promised each other that sometime in the future they would meet again and begin their life together. Eventually time marched on and the months turned to years. The young lovers grew older. Rosa settled into her new life in Italy but she never forgot Alessandro as she faced a series of eligible young men who came knocking at the farm's door. Rosa's family became much wealthier as the large farm began to adopt more modern farming methods. Rosa was a good catch but much to her parent's annoyance she turned down all advances and marriage proposals. The two lovers continued to write to each other.

Alessandro was 27 years old when the First World War broke out and his dutiful friends immediately began to sign up to fight for their King and Country. Alessandro was friendly with many of the donkey boys, they all tried to encourage him to also fulfil his duty. Most local tradesmen that he'd come to know and respect over the years all signed up too and they encouraged him to do likewise. Eventually Alessandro's friends, colleagues, customers, and family began to ask lots of awkward questions. He'd always been a deeply religious young man. His Catholic faith was particularly strong and he just couldn't bring himself to do what his King and Country expected of him. He argued endlessly with everyone who pressed him to do the right thing. "It's not right, I could never forgive myself if I shot and killed another man." Alessandro would lie awake at night pondering upon his convictions and his dreams became restless and tormented. Over time many friends, colleagues and customers shunned him. Being a conscientious objector was not an easy path; it was both lonely and dangerous. In 1915 and again in 1916 local gangs attacked him late at night as he made his way home from his carpentry workshop. Only Rosa, his faithful sweetheart, was sympathetic to his convictions. She understood Alessandro's heart and knew only too well that he could never put himself in a position where he was asked to take another person's life be they friend or foe.

Every year his family would travel north on the train to Tyneside to visit Italian relatives who'd also immigrated. It was during such a visit in the summer of 1917 that Alessandro heard about ships leaving Tyneside on a regular schedule. They carried coal and were bound for Italy. With Rosa's help he hatched a plan. He decided to return to Margate, put his affairs in order, then venture back to Tyneside and stow away on one of these steamships. After much thought Alessandro decided to share his plan with Juliana, his mother. They were closely bonded and he felt that he just couldn't disappear without saying goodbye and sharing his future plans. On one hand Juliana was happy that her only son was leaving his difficult situation in Margate because of his pacifist convictions. He was going to join the love of his life but on the other hand she was really quite alarmed. She knew that her son was afraid of deep water and couldn't swim. She agonized endlessly upon the possibility that something could happen to his steamship and that he might fall into the ocean and drown. It was her greatest fear. Eventually she took matters into her own hands and made enquiries amongst the local fisherman who sat on the harbour quayside mending their nets. One of them agreed to sell her the new life vest that he'd recently acquired. As she handed over a sizable sum from her savings the seasoned fisherman knew better than to ask too many questions. He was glad of the extra cash to help feed his large family and there would be plenty left over to pay his bar bill at The Benjamin Beale Public House down by the harbour.

Juliana begged Alessandro to take the life vest with him and wear it during his voyage. He reluctantly agreed but, in his heart, he knew that it was far too bulky and not something that a stowaway could easily hide. His distraught mother sensed an ill wind pass over her shoulders, as she stood on the platform at Margate's train station one bright blustery day in mid-October. She waved and blew farewell kisses but her heart felt heavy as she held back her tears. She hoped and prayed with all her heart that she would see her much-loved son again one day. However, deep down she almost knew that this might be her last glimpse as Alessandro leaned out of the window smiling and blew her one last kiss.

Alessandro wasn't without reservations. The prospect of a voyage over deep water frightened him. He'd never cared much for boats and he knew that he couldn't swim. It was wartime and he'd read in the newspapers that German U-boats were attacking supply ships. If anything happened to his ship, he knew that he would be lost forever. His heart felt heavy. He'd said goodbyes to his mother, the town he'd come to love and to his successful business. It was a very tall order. He was about to risk everything to be with Rosa in Italy.

Once back in Tyneside Alessandro began to frequent public houses down by the docks. He listened intently to the sailors' conversations at the bar and after a few days he learnt that the SS Gallia, carrying a cargo of 3,029 tons of coal, was leaving port soon and bound for Savona in Italy. He quickly befriended a couple of her crewmembers plying them with glasses of Macallan Single Malt Scotch Whisky. After several days he'd gathered a great deal of information pertaining to the collier. The well-known Sunderland ship builders Bartram, Haswell & Co built SS Gallia of steel. The new steamship was completed in 1887 with a gross tonnage of 2,728 and powered by a three-cylinder triple expansion engine with a single shaft and one propeller. Interestingly she began her maritime life as SS Olive Branch. Alessandro really liked that given his pacifist views! The Nautilus Steamship Company owned her from 1887 until 1914 when she was sold to Medici Lucotti Cerrano from Genoa who changed her name to SS Gallia. Another change of ownership followed and her present owner was Federazione Italiana dei Consortzi Agrari of Genoa.

Alessandro's newfound drinking friends eagerly shared with him all the details that he needed to know. He learnt her deck plans, crew details, where she was docked, the security procedures in place and the exact day and time of her sailing. With all this information at his fingertips he hatched his plan. The collier was due to leave in a few days. This left him just enough time to gather supplies for his voyage. He purchased tinned and dried food and some fresh apples and pears to see him through. He also bought a tin plate, bowl, mug and cutlery. He knew that a water supply was kept in barrels on the deck and planned to help himself late at night under the cover of darkness when only a skeleton watch crew were on duty. His supplies were carefully packed tightly into a haversack. He planned to hide underneath one of the lifeboats on the deck. However, Alessandro agonized over the life vest that his mother had insisted that he brought along and that he'd reluctantly promised to wear. It was simply far too bulky. He already had an over filled haversack and a knapsack stuffed full of clothes. He felt bad, he was breaking a promise, but if he was to keep himself hidden and avoid discovery there was really no room for mother's life vest.

In the late afternoon, the day before SS Gallia was due to leave port, Alessandro settled up with his landlady. Ethel Hopewell was elderly; her husband had passed away before the war. She owned the boarding house where he'd taken a room. He handed her a large canvas bag stuffed with some of his clothes and the bulky life vest. Alessandro explained, "I need to leave town in a hurry. Please look after this bag. My mother visits relatives on Tyneside every summer I'll be sending her your address and she'll stop by next summer to collect." Ethel was a little taken aback when he confided that he was leaving town in a hurry. She knew that he had been out drinking every night since his arrival. His room smelled of stale cigarettes and whisky. She looked down very doubtfully upon the heavy canvas bag. However, when Alessandro pulled out a golden guinea Ethel's stance began to soften. She was mindful that these were hard and difficult times and, in the end, money spoke volumes. Ethel sighed, looked him in the eye and simply said, "Take care of yourself young man. I'll keep this bag safely here until your mother pays me a visit." Alessandro nodded in gratitude and on his way to the docks he stopped to post a hastily written letter to Juliana.

Dearest Mother,

I leave tonight on SS Gallia. She's a collier bound for Savona. I befriended the crew and know all about this fine steamship. I propose to hide underneath one of the lifeboats. Unfortunately, space is limited and I have to leave behind your life vest and a number of clothing items. Ethel, the landlady at my boarding house, has graciously agreed to keep them safe until you manage to return to Tyneside next summer to collect them.

Here is her address:

Ethel Hopewell
42 Risk Street, Newcastle upon Tyne

Until we meet again,

Your ever-loving son, Alessandro

By the time that Juliana received his letter the SS Gallia had sunk. On October 24, 1917 a large explosion occurred on the port side penetrating the engine room and she quickly went down. The crew didn't know at the time if a mine or a torpedo had hit her. They quickly abandoned the stricken ship. Most of them got away in a large lifeboat while the pilot officer and a few other men left in the gig. The men from both boats were picked up by the patrol vessel Wyndham and landed at Weymouth around 9 pm. The captain and 5 of her crew were injured and taken to the local hospital. It was originally reported that two of her crew were lost but one, the cook, had been rescued from the water by the trawler Florence and transferred to another fishing boat that landed him ashore. He was taken to the hospital at Seaton. The German submarine that claimed to sink the SS Gallia was UB - 40 commanded by Hans Howaldt who eventually sank 63 ships over his career. SS Gallia was one of 13 Italian steamships lost within the forgotten wrecks project area during the war. Of these 13, 8 were recorded as carrying coal at the time of their loss.

When all was said and done the possibility of Alessandro's survival had been slim. The torpedo struck the port side where he was hiding underneath a lifeboat. The force of the sudden explosion violently shook the steamship and as she lurched to one side he slid from beneath the boat onto the deck and toppled into the water. It all happened so quickly. He'd kept his presence on board secret. Although he'd befriended several crewmembers on shore at the public house, he'd never confided in them. They thought that his interest in their ship was purely friendly conversation. As Alessandro slid into the water his cries for help were unnoticed as pandemonium and fire broke out on SS Gallia. As some of her crewmembers floundered in the water no one searched for Alessandro. The ocean took him swiftly under and in his dying moments his mind turned to Juliana and the life vest that he'd left behind. If only he'd been wearing that life vest, he might have had the future that he'd yearned and planned for.

That night, Wednesday October 24, 1917, Juliana had retired early to bed. Her sleep was particularly restless and just before midnight she had a nightmare. Alessandro was standing beside her bed. He was soaking wet and extremely distraught. He kept muttering over and over again, "I'm so very sorry. I'm so very sorry. I love you, please forgive me." She woke with a start as her clock struck midnight. Juliana climbed out of bed and turned on her lamp. She was most surprised when she noticed a large puddle of cold water on the bare floorboards at the end of her bed. She drew the curtains and looked out of her window. The sky was lit up as the full moon was approaching but there had been no rain that night. She looked up at her ceiling to see if there had been a plumbing leak but there was no evidence of damage. As she knelt down and began to examine the puddle of water her heart began to pound. Deep in her inner knowing she realized that something awful had happened to her Alessandro.

The next few days Juliana scoured the papers. Eventually she noticed a headline in a London newspaper.

SS Gallia hit and sunk by a German U - Boat on Oct 24

Juliana took her only son's death very badly. He lay somewhere at the bottom of the ocean in an unmarked, watery grave. He'd joined so many of his friends who had gone to war and died in some distant foreign place far away from home and their loved ones. Her sleep remained restless and disturbed. She took it upon herself to write to his beloved Rosa and break the bad news. Towards Christmas time, still deeply grieving, she took a train to Tyneside to seek out Ethel and bring home what was left of Alessandro.

Juliana clung to the life vest for several months. She agonized over her son's broken promise and his bad decision. She questioned God many times as she clung to her rosary beads. "Why my son?" In the end her terrible grief ate away at her like an acid. It destroyed what hope she had in a future. Her health rapidly declined. Sadly, by the time that the spring flowers were in full bloom the gravediggers at the Margate Cemetery were preparing her final resting place. Her husband, Benigno was more stoic, he'd never really forgiven Alessandro for his pacifist stance and for turning his back on Margate. He mourned the passing of his darling wife. Of course, he missed his only son but he became extremely bitter and angry. He carefully wrapped the life vest in sturdy brown paper, placed it in the canvas sail bag along with Alessandro's clothes and stashed them far away in the roof space of their little home on Milton Avenue. "Out of sight and out of mind!" He muttered to himself. Tragically he never spoke of Alessandro again.

A teardrop rolled down Maria's cheek as she opened her eyes and looked down at the old life vest. This was such a sad story of a broken promise and the dire consequences that followed. Her heart ached for Juliana and Benigno and for Rosa too who'd so looked forward to a joyful reunion with her sweetheart. She'd made so many plans for their future together in Italy. Maria's mind suddenly turned to all the willing, innocent, young men who'd left the Isle of Thanet bound for France. Her heart ached for all those who still lay in known and unknown graves on foreign soil and for those who'd returned as broken men unable to live a normal life again. The sensitive, controversial issues around those who chose to fight and those who stood their ground and chose the way of the pacifist troubled her greatly. War was such a terrible thing. The First World War robbed a generation of young souls and for those who'd chosen a peaceful path their families had often been torn apart. Young men were ostracized and cast out. Fathers, forced to hang their heads in shame, abandoned their sons. Maria ran her ancient, wrinkled hands over the life vest one more time. It emanated vibrations of intense painful sadness and a sorrow so great that it couldn't be contained. Maria turned to Jack the Lad who was snuggled up on his velvet cushion next to her armchair and muttered, "How ironic that something made purposely by willing hands to save lives never had the opportunity to serve. Instead, it became a symbol of broken promises, disgrace and palpable heartache."

As she rose from her armchair she sighed and felt so terribly old. Maria took Poppy aside and briefly recounted Alessandro's tale. "Poppy you're so right this life vest exudes such troubled energy. It doesn't belong here in the shop and we cannot pass it onto others. It may cause more havoc. I will take it to my old allotment garden and burn it. Fire can be so transformative. I will pray for all those involved in its troubled history that they are now at peace. I've been so very busy in Key West. I've a lovely new vintage shop set up in a grand old house called St. Eustace. Good people have come to help me, there's much work to be done. You were quite right to call me and ask for help. Remember that I'll always come if you need me, so until the next time I bid you farewell." Maria turned to Jack the Lad and tickled his ear then she strode out of the door with the life vest tucked firmly under her arm.

Poppy felt that a huge burden had been lifted from her shoulders. Madam Popoff had taught her so much over the years. She'd grown to understand the nature of energy and ownership. She knew that it was important to screen old things as they came into the shop for resale to ensure that her customers weren't inheriting some troubled karma. That night while she lay in bed at Lookout Retreat, she reflected upon the tragic story that the life vest held in its exergy field. She thought about Dr. Bach and his 38 flower essences. She'd learnt how very helpful the essences were because they covered the whole gamut of human emotions. She'd read that in 1917 Dr. Bach was a war surgeon in charge of 400 beds at a big London hospital and how he later brought forth what he called the superior healers of mankind. Poppy had come to realize the important place that emotions play in health and healing and how helpful these essences can be.

Thinking about Juliana she thought about the Bach flower *Red Chestnut,* often helpful when one is continually anxious for loved ones and *Star of Bethlehem,* for shock, trauma and grief. She also remembered the homeopathic remedies *Ignatia* for acute grief and loss and the deeper remedy, *Phosphoric Acid,* that can often follow when grief is not processed continuing to eat away like an acid undermining the constitution because there's an inability to move on. Poppy wondered if only a homeopathic doctor had been able to administer these helpful remedies perhaps Alessandro's mother would have been able to visualize a future without her son and wouldn't have faced such an early death. Then her mind turned to Benigno. She reflected upon his anger and resentment and the sad fact that he never mentioned his son again. She wondered if the flower essence *Holly* would have helped to open up his heart and *Willow* to help let go of his resentment and bitterness, enabling him to forgive and to forget. Then as she turned over to go to sleep, she realized that in 1917 the Bach essences had yet to be discovered.

Sponges

Mid October was quickly approaching. The balmy Florida Keys weather enticed the retired wealthy snowbirds to return. They hailed from far-flung places up in the north where icy winds and the threat of snow meant many months of long cold days and nights. "Well, you can't blame them!" Exclaimed Desmond to Henry, Ruth's spunky Jack Russell Terrier. Henry had established himself in St. Eustace's vintage shop. Desmond found him an old velvet cushion and he liked to sun himself on the deep window seat peering out and keeping a watchful eye on all the visitors approaching the house.

Desmond had adapted very quickly to his new job. Every day was different and every day something mysterious and magical seemed to occur. The enigmatic Madam Popoff had taken him aside shortly after the St. Eustace feast day grand celebration opening and enlightened him. "Desmond, many things that we sell in this shop belonged to someone else, they all have a story to tell. Some of those stories are good, some bad and some ugly, evil even. Mark my word there are things that we simply cannot pass along because their energy is too disturbing. You need to develop the powers of discernment. Run your fingers over the merchandise, meditate and pray for guidance. If you get a hunch that something doesn't feel right then investigate further. We want our customers to take their new found treasures home and enjoy them."

At first Desmond had been taken aback by Maria's revelations. Nevertheless, he began to heed her words of warning and gave it all careful thought. He called and shared his concerns with his friends up in New York. He really liked Maria. She was so very old yet wise, gracious and extremely kind. Many old people shunned him because he was gay, even his own family. He felt at home in St. Eustace, he could be himself and didn't have to worry about being constantly ostracized. He decided to act upon her words of warning and began to experiment. He would sit with some treasure that he pulled off the shelf or the clothing rack and hold it in his hands. He shut his eyes and began to meditate. He asked to know more and gradually over a number of days information began to filter through. He became fascinated by Maria's guidance because it opened up a whole new world of insight. Secrets began to surface. Strange stories revealed much of life's ups and downs and as Maria had initially instructed there was always the good, the bad, the ugly and even the evil. Desmond acquired a large cardboard box that he kept behind the counter. This was where he stored any questionable merchandise until Maria had time to investigate further. She would cast her eye over everything and vote if it could stay or if it should make a swift exit out to the bonfire area. Fred had established a suitable area at the back of St. Eustace and such potentially disturbing items were to be quickly disposed of.

Key West residents, clearing out their attics and cupboards, began to drop bags and boxes off at St. Eustace's door. Often this happened late at night and a variety of unwanted things were usually stuffed into large black plastic bin liners. A number of treasures began to surface from the local area's fascinating history. Since the early days of its settlement sea related businesses were the lifeblood of this growing community at the end of America. Shipping, shipbuilding, fishing, turtling, sponging, salt production and wrecking were an important and a vital part of the economy. There were hundreds of ships in the harbour or anchored off shore. Once upon a time Key West was the most affluent city in the whole of Florida! The harbour had four entranceways 14 - 33 feet deep and these allowed ships sailing the trade routes to visit. Ships brought immigrants from northern states as well as from the Bahamas and Cuba. Today the lively harbour is packed with all kinds of watercraft. There's the regular fishing fleet but pleasure craft and fancy mega yachts belonging to the rich and famous have taken over what berths are left. Then there's the large deep-sea sport fishing boats that wealthy tourists pay a fortune to hire. Several beautiful historic schooners are also tied up at the quayside just like the one that Ruth worked on at the weekends.

Today, Friday October 15th, Desmond arrived early even before Ruth had opened up the café for the morning trade. Regulars now dropped by for their coffee and freshly baked croissants and pastries. St. Eustace had quickly become the smart go to place for the young and fashionable to meet up, socialize and exchange business ideas. Tourists were beginning to discover the delightful café too.

Today Desmond found a very large narrow cardboard box sitting on the doorstep. It was quite light despite its size. He took it inside and after finishing his early morning clean up chores around the shop he settled down with a cup of coffee. He had an hour to spare before opening time so he decided to examine the contents. Much to his surprise it was packed with old sponges and a rather strange looking wooden pole with a three-pronged rake on one end. Desmond wondered if this was somehow connected with the sponge fishing industry that began in the early settlement period of Key West back in the 19th century. He laid the long pole across his lap, fingered it gently, shut his eyes and slowly drifted off and back to another time.

Pioneer settlers began to inhabit Key West, also known as Cayo Hueso meaning Bone Cay, in 1822. US businessman, John Simonton, was able to gain clear title to the island at that time. He had business interests in Mobile, Alabama and bought the island after he became aware of its strategic maritime location. The coral island was covered in bones from prior native inhabitants who'd used it as a communal graveyard. The early settlers had to gradually clear them out. By 1829 a post office and newspaper were in business. Kurt's great grandfather began their family business in those early days of pioneer settlement. The sponge industry began in the 1820's when fishermen discovered sponges washed up on the shores after storms. In those early days a small fleet of boats evolved. They were called *hook boats* because a log pole with a three or four-pronged rake on the end was used to hook sponges from the shallow waters. At first the sponges were used locally for domestic use but in 1849 a sample shipment was sent to New York and found a ready market. As a result, the sponge industry expanded as demand increased. By the time of Kurt's birth in 1890 Key West had the monopoly of sponge trade in America. At that time, it was recorded that some 350 *hook boats* operated out of Key West and 1400 men were employed in the industry. Nearly all of the sponges were collected from the surrounding shallow waters. However, as the industry expanded the sponge boats ventured further afield into the Gulf of Mexico where the seabed was covered with sponges of all different varieties. During the Spanish American War of 1898, because of their fear of Spanish warships, the entire Key West sponge fleet put into Tarpon Springs up on the western coast of mainland Florida to sell their sponge cargo. The Key West sponging grounds were by this time becoming depleted and Tarpon Springs quickly took over the lead in sponge production.

Kurt's father, George, inherited the family business around the time that his wife Elsie gave birth to their second son. From a very young age Kurt and his older brother Dan went out on the sponge fishing expeditions. He loved to watch the pelicans flying low above the waves in elegant formation as they sought out a good catch. At the turn of the century, upon his tenth birthday, he was given his first proper job in the family business. Kurt and Dan would spend hours at the weekends and after school laying out the sponges to dry in the hot Florida sunshine. By the end of the day, as the sun began to set, their work was done. They'd carefully sorted and packed the sponges into wooden crates to be shipped to far off destinations. It was hard work. Occasionally the brothers were allowed out on the *hook boats* to help spear the sponges with a long pole. Kurt particularly loved these expeditions. He always felt so good when he was out on the ocean with the warm, salty breeze rippling through his hair. Ospreys, Merlins and Peregrine Falcons would circle overhead and he listened intently to the Seagull's piercing cries. Kurt often smiled to himself and believed that his tropical island home with its sparkling white beaches and tall coconut palm trees swaying gently in the sea breeze was paradise.

However, Kurt's elderly grandfather remembered times when paradise had been destroyed. One evening, at the turn of the century and shortly after his tenth birthday, he took Kurt aside and told the curious boy stories from the early days. With clay pipe in his hand and sitting in his comfortable armchair he turned to Kurt and said, "It wasn't always that easy Kurt. In October 1841 a hurricane raised the tide in the Key West harbour higher than any one had ever remembered, and wrecked ships along the Lower Keys. A year later another hurricane struck the Lower Keys and damaged the Sand Key lighthouse and numerous navigation beacons. In October 1844 a storm called the Cuban Hurricane, moved up the Keys causing considerable damage. Many of the structures built by the Navy on Indian Key and all of the wharves were reported as washed away. Then back in October 1846 there was a really devastating hurricane. They called it The Great Havana Hurricane because it blasted out of Cuba 90 miles away like an out-of-control steam train. It ripped across the Florida Straits until it hit the Lower Keys. Both the Sand Key and Key West lighthouses were destroyed. No occupants survived that terrible day. It destroyed all but eight of the 600 buildings on the island at that time. Water rose to about eight feet in the lower town streets and it washed dead bodies from the cemetery, which at that time was located out on coastal sand dunes on Whitehead Point. Building supplies and skilled carpenters were in short supply and we had to start again rebuilding the town once more mainly using salvaged lumber.

Of course, there's been other events since but none as bad and as fatal as the Great Havana. Nature is a powerful force, Kurt. Not only can it bestow life and sustain livelihoods but also it can just as quickly whisk it all away in the blink of an eye. It can rob us of our loved ones, our homes and our livelihoods. All that's left are fond memories and many very broken pieces. In truth paradise is fragile and we are all vulnerable living on this beautiful piece of coral just four miles long and 150 miles from mainland Florida. You must enjoy it, savour every day and be thankful while you can. Remember to thank God for every day that your life is blessed in paradise. After the 1846 hurricane many sponges were washed up on the shore and they were a blessing. They helped to rebuild my business. They provided food for our table and money for your grandma to eventually visit the store and purchase some luxuries. A word of warning Kurt, always respect the sea and the winds. Learn to watch the weather carefully, always pray for guidance and make for the shore in plenty of time. Heed your own inner compass when it tells you to seek shelter. Mother Nature can be so unforgiving when she's angry." Grandfather suddenly looked very weary, he closed his eyes and began to shudder as if someone had walked over his grave.

As Kurt grew into a young man life became more difficult for the family sponge business because shallow sponge beds around the Lower Keys became more and more depleted. During this time Tarpon Springs, located on the Gulf of Mexico on the west coast of Florida, quickly established itself as the focus of the sponge industry. John Corcosis was born in Greece and in 1895 he came to New York to work in the sponge trade. He met John Cheyney in the city; John was one of the early settlers in Tarpon Springs. He'd sent out the first *hooker boat* in the town. The two men formed a partnership and Corcosis insisted that they brought sponge divers over from Greece to the Tarpon Springs community so that sponges at deeper depths could be accessed. Sponge divers in Greece had been harvesting sponges for centuries in the eastern Mediterranean but a diving suit with a helmet and air hoses had been introduced in 1865 allowing them to harvest at much deeper levels. So, in 1905 the first colony of Greek sponge divers established themselves. At that time the sponge diving industry had grown to its maximum in Greece and its native divers were looking for employment elsewhere so many families were ready and willing to immigrate to America. They bought with them hard-hat diving, plans of their Mediterranean sponge boats and other paraphernalia. Eventually Tarpon Springs became the sponge capital of America.

Sadly, Kurt's beloved grandfather also passed away early in 1905 and was buried in the town cemetery. Kurt was fifteen years old at the time. Major family discussions, sometimes turning into heated arguments, followed. They faced a major financial crisis. There seemed to be one of two solutions on the table. Either they all relocate to Tarpon Springs and learn to use the diving suits or they remain in Key West. If they remained, they would also have to learn to use the diving suits because the local sponge beds were becoming more and more depleted. The other option was to completely reinvent the family business. Key West was quickly losing its allure and becoming less of a paradise. Money was in such short supply. George wondered how he could pay the bills that were quickly mounting up on the kitchen dresser. Each day their family-owned *hook boats* returned with a mere handful of sponges. Their livelihood had become severely depleted. However, in truth, no one wanted to leave. The family had established themselves on this piece of coral far away from mainland Florida for several generations. Kurt's great grandparents and now his grandfather were all buried in the local cemetery. Grandma refused to leave complaining bitterly and telling them all in no uncertain terms, "This is where I was born! This is my home. This is where I belong. This is where our family have strong roots and this is where I will be put in the ground when my time finally comes!"

With the family's matriarch digging in her heels there seemed very little choice. Leaving was not an option for Kurt, Dan and the rest of the family. 1905 proved to be an extremely interesting year for Key West and its residents. Following the United States Government's construction of the Panama Canal, which had begun the previous year on May 04, 1904, the extremely wealthy, successful and prominent oil magnate, Henry Morrison Flagler, announced that he was very interested in linking Key West to mainland Florida. Flagler was a visionary and he could see that Key West was the closest deep-water port in America to the new canal project, which eventually took ten years of hard labour to complete. In 1905 the port of Key West was already taking advantage of Cuban and Latin American trade. However, with the eventual opening of the Panama Canal a whole new world of trade possibilities with America's west coast would be available for exploitation. Flagler's proposed Overseas Railroad would be an extension of his already successful Florida East Coast Railway.

Back in 1885 the oil magnate, who had started the Standard Oil Company in 1870 with John D. Rockefeller, had purchased a short line railroad operating on Florida's east coast between Jacksonville and St. Augustine. Over time Flagler extended his railroad south to Miami. By 1904 it had reached the southern community of Homestead and now he planned to extend it over the chain of islands to Key West. Few people supported the ambitious idea and many thought he was crazy. They dubbed it *Flagler's Folly*. Nevertheless, the successful business tycoon decided to push ahead and construction began in 1905.

This proposed new railroad actually became the much-needed lifesaver for Kurt and his family. *Flagler's Folly* became the talk of the town and like so many other strong, fit, young men living in the Florida Keys at the time Kurt and Dan signed up along with George, their father. It was a multi-million-dollar investment for Flagler and his business associates and its construction required tremendous manpower. Flagler's workers were required to create something out of nothing as they built roadbeds, bridges and viaducts through water, sand and swamp over 128 miles. Camps were established for the thousands of labourers who worked day and night on the construction. Over the next seven years the men had to deal with the threat of hurricanes, alligators, rattlesnakes, sand flies, and mosquitos. Building a railroad in the middle of water required a fleet of ships. Flagler's armada included launches, houseboats, steamers and workboats complete with cranes and pile drivers. Everything had to be ferried to the worksites. Ocean-going vessels transported raw materials from Florida's mainland. George knew that this was the window of opportunity that they'd desperately prayed for.

His family had been seafarers for generations. George knew the waters surrounding the Florida Keys like the back of his hand. He understood what charts were available at the time and knew where all the major sand banks and wrecks were located. Most important of all he understood the weather patterns and his natural instinct had always taught him when to head for shore and batten down the hatches.

George spotted *The Margaret Anne* rotting away in a small hidden corner of the Key West harbour around the same time that his father had passed away. At one time, in her heyday, the large 80-foot sturdy clinker-built screw-propelled steam trawler supported the many families who worked her. However, tragically she now lay at rest lonely, forgotten and abandoned. Despite his many enquiries George was unable to discover what had happened to her owners. The fate of

The Margaret Anne remained a mystery. The Harbour Master reported that she had lain neglected for at least three years and he speculated that the family may have moved up north in a hurry and for some mysterious reason they'd abandoned her. He couldn't understand why because she had been such a fine boat. "I heard that she originally crossed over the Atlantic in the late 1880's from the large fishing port of Grimsby in northern England. She's clinker built meaning the outer planks of the hull are overlapped so she's stronger and safer in stormy weather. She's also lighter since there's less internal framing. Of course, being lighter she displaces less water so she's faster too. George, she's certainly a good boat if you can fix her up!"

Following extended negotiations with the harbour authorities and a lot of paperwork George eventually received permission to take charge of the abandoned vessel as long as he agreed to repair and maintain her and paid her docking dues. He went straight to the bank and requested a loan. *The Margaret Anne* would require a great deal of work and care to ensure that she was still sea worthy. He suspected that she might even need a new engine. George knew that he was in a favourable negotiating position because Flagler needed supply boats. He knew that with his sons' help he could run her up and down the Keys ferrying supplies from Key West and Florida's mainland to the work camps. Flagler was prepared to pay good money and this was how the family could reinvent themselves and remain in Key West. *The Margaret Anne* would be their salvation.

When Flagler's name was mentioned the bank manager came through with an initial loan enabling George to purchase the necessary wood, paint and various tools needed to refit her. For the first time in over a year George smiled and sighed with relief as he began to visualize a future for his family in the place, they all loved. He visited *The Basilica of St. Mary Star of the Sea* on the corner of Duval and Eaton Streets to give thanks and to pray for more help to get her up and running. *The Margaret Anne* had really suffered over three years of neglect. The blistering heat of the Florida sun had been relentlessly unforgiving. Periods of stormy weather had thrown her up against the stone quayside so she presented in a very sorry state. "She's got so many broken pieces and I'm particularly worried about the state of her steam engine. I know that the bank loan won't stretch to the purchase of a new engine," George anxiously confided to Dan and Kurt one evening.

Just as they were preparing to begin renovations Cousin Mike stepped forward. He'd always kept the family at a distance. George considered him to be an angry, disillusioned man who preferred his own company. However, Mike was a skilled carpenter and one day, much to George's surprise, he appeared on the dock with his tool bag announcing that he'd come to help. Mike volunteered to help repair much of the rotten wood discovered throughout her hull. He proved to be a true blessing in disguise. Over the next few weeks other family friends also pitched in. Within three weeks *The Margaret Anne* was beginning to shape up really nicely. Repairs to her wooden hull were complete. Many hands had helped to paint her and now she sported a beautiful royal blue and sparkling white livery. She also had a new compass, anchor, sails and docking lines. It was wonderful how many people generously offered to help. Many Key West boatmen stopped by each day to watch the progress. They all loved their boats. There was an energetic connection to that which sustained their families and brought them safely home each night. None of them felt good about a boat that had been abandoned and left to rot away in a forgotten corner of the harbour.

George still continued to worry about the state of her steam engine. The hull and paintwork had consumed all of his energy and attention over the past three weeks but now it was time to tackle her engine. He decided to visit *St Mary's Basilica* once again and pray for help as his intuition told him that all was not well with the engine and he had absolutely no experience working on these steam engines. He wasn't sure whom he could ask for help. *The Margaret Anne* would be going nowhere unless her high-pressure steam engine with return flues was dependable. Of course, she had sails too but Flagler needed boats that could deliver quickly and reliably.

His prayers were quickly addressed because old Alfred miraculously appeared the very next day. He'd recently joined his brother's family and retired to a small place on Duval Street. As Alfred had sat outside the family home smoking his clay pipe neighbours told him about all the recent activity down at the docks and the transformation of *The Margaret Anne.* Alfred had grown up in New York and spent all of his working life in shipyards up in Buffalo, New York. He'd worked on the construction of steam-powered tugs and over the years he'd learnt to repair their engines. Just like Cousin Mike, Alfred was the gift that George had prayed for.

Alfred was curious and he stopped by to see for himself the work in progress. It didn't take him long to agree to volunteer his time. Some welding of broken pipes and cleaning out of clogged, corroded valves was necessary and a few extra parts were ordered from the local hardware store. However, within a few weeks Alfred had the steam engine up and running. He was actually glad that he had something to do. Retirement had not lived up to his expectations. He has bored and missed the camaraderie of men folk. Plenty of people were stopping by each day to watch the progress. Many bystanders wanted to know more about the steam engine and Alfred relished the attention and the opportunity to share his knowledge and teach. In the twilight of his years, he felt useful once again. His aches and pains disappeared and he woke up each day with a spring in his step and a renewed sense of life purpose.

When all was said and done George began to realize that *The Margaret Anne* was not only his own family's salvation. At supper that night he made his announcement to the family gathered around the table. "She's brought our Key West community together in friendship and the act of giving. We all have different talents. We all need a purpose, a reason for getting up every day and in her transformation, she has brought something very special and beautiful in her wake." It was Kurt's sudden idea to change her name. "Father, *The Margaret Anne* is indeed a very special lady. I know you've been to the Basilica several times asking for help. She's been a blessing to so many of us and there's no doubt that your prayers have been answered. Perhaps we should change her name to *Mary Star of the Sea?*" Everyone smiled and agreed that it was a grand idea. That night whilst in bed George reflected upon all that had happened over the past few months. He thought it particularly strange that when she'd been painted in her new royal blue and sparkling white livery no one had bothered to repaint her name on the stern or the bow. "So, *Mary Star of the Sea*, it is," he smiled and muttered to himself. The next day Kurt and Dan took it upon themselves to carefully paint her new name in gold italics. "*Mary Star of the Sea, Key West.*"

Now, with old Alfred and Cousin Mike's help, when the occasion arose, *Mary Star of the Sea* plied up and down the coast ferrying supplies between the work camps, Florida's mainland and Key West for the next seven years. She proved to be a stable, reliable boat. The men in the work camps looked forward to her arrival because most of her cargo was food for the camp kitchens or medical supplies. She took Dan, Kurt and George away from home for many months at a time. However, over time she generated a stable income for the family and for the extra crew that were sometimes needed. As roadbeds grew from the sea and tracks were laid the job became much easier. Now workers and equipment could be brought to the construction site over the completed tracks. Land based worksites were erected that had previously been under the water.

Mary Star of the Sea managed to weather and survive two devastating hurricanes and remained reasonably intact. Kurt always wondered if she enjoyed some sort of special spiritual protection because other ships docked nearby were smashed to pieces. On October 11th, 1909, one of the most intense hurricanes ever recorded to that date in Florida hit the Keys. Winds were clocked at 94 miles per hour, accompanied by 8 to 10 inches of rain. At Sand Key the weather bureau building was swept out to sea and in Key West more than 400 buildings were washed away by the tide or collapsed due to the high winds. Before the bad weather hit the family did their best to secure her to the stone quayside using a complex arrangement of ropes to keep her from hitting the wall but also allowing her to rise with the level of the water should a storm surge occur. The next day George, Dan and Kurt tentatively picked their way through streets filled with debris and fallen telegraph poles. All this devastation fuelled their escalating anxiety as they made their way down to the harbour. To their horror more than 300 boats had been destroyed but miraculously *Mary Star of the Sea* in her royal blue and sparkling white livery remained intact. Several fishermen were standing around in the knee-high mud and wooden debris on the quayside commiserating with each other. Joe nodded and broke away from the gathering. He waded over to George and patting him on the back he said, "Your lady luck must have a very special angel sitting on her bow. Look around you George, everything else has been smashed to smithereens!" The city of Key West reported over one million dollars in damage from the hurricane. Portions of Flagler's completed railroad were washed away so it seemed to everyone involved that the work took them two steps forward and one step backwards.

When another hurricane hit the following year and carried away many of the structures that survived the destructive 1909 storm George lamented, "It's like pouring salt on an open wound. Here we are again picking up all these broken pieces. It takes a very special breed of people to endure such hardship and stay on this piece of coral at the end of America!" George, Dan and Kurt were always ready and willing to help their neighbours and offer shelter too when needed. The men helped others rebuild whilst always pondering the fate of their own special boat. Kurt often asked Dan, "Why does she always remain intact?" Following such adversity, the family made it a regular habit to slip into *St Mary's Basilica* to give thanks.

Finally, on January 22nd, 1912 the Florida East Coast Railroad's Extension Special, pulling Flagler's private coach arrived in Key West. Huge crowds gathered excitedly on the streets to celebrate. George and his family dressed in their Sunday best clothes. They waved and cheered as Flagler, now elderly and frail, stepped out of the carriage to greet the crowds. Some called his railway *The Eighth Wonder of the World.* It had cost an estimated 25 million dollars and employed almost

4,000 men but it had also sadly taken the lives of hundreds of workers in the process. Working conditions for the majority had not been good at all. The unforgiving Florida sun and the ever threat of bad storms and those two hurricanes, together with poisonous snakes, alligators, mosquito borne diseases and infections robbed families of their loved ones. Flagler was unable to enjoy his great accomplishment for long as the following year on May 20th he passed away in West Palm Beach. He'd been a generous man who wanted to create opportunities for others. He donated money to build schools, hospitals and churches and to provide relief to farmers after freezes destroyed their produce. Most of his donations were made anonymously. He was buried in St. Augustine, Florida.

Seven years of relentlessly hard work had also taken its toll upon George. Exhausted and looking much older than his fifty-five years he decided it was finally time to step back and retire. Flagler's railroad had enabled the family to save a considerable sum of money. Henry Flagler had been a reliable employer. The initial bank loan to refurbish *Mary Star of the Sea* had been repaid. It was time to pass the boat that had brought them nothing but good luck over to Dan and Kurt's care and once again it was time for the two brothers to reinvent the family business. Flagler's Overseas Railroad began to open up Key West to very wealthy tourists and there were always plenty of Cuban families who wanted to travel back and forth to Cuba some 90 nautical miles away. As predicted Flagler's railroad had enhanced trade relations between Cuba and Key West. The two brothers planned to establish a private ferry service. They could easily accommodate 10-12 passengers along with their luggage for the 90-mile crossing across the Florida Strait.

Eventually the two brothers married and began families of their own. Kurt was almost thirty years old and a seasoned boat captain with a wife and two young daughters to support when the devastating hurricane of September 1919 hit. It formed on September 2nd near the Leeward Islands and gradually gained strength passing the Florida Keys on September 9 -10th. The storm's slow movement and sheer size prolonged and enlarged the scope of the hurricane's effects making it one of the deadliest in the recorded history of the United States. Impacts were largely concentrated around the Florida Keys and the South Texas coast but Cuba also felt its effects. There was a strong storm surge in Havana that topped the sea wall and areas of the city were flooded. The hurricane's peak strength, probably a category 4 in modern times with a high wind speed of 149 mph, was when it passed over the Dry Tortugas in the Lower Florida Keys. It also made it one of the most powerful Atlantic hurricanes to make landfall in the United States and caused 22 million dollars' worth of damage.

Communication was cut off for the entirety of Florida south of Miami following the storm's passage. Of the approximately 600-900 people officially reported killed in the storm, roughly 500 of them were aboard ten ships lost at sea. The steamer *SS Valbanera* was found sunk between Key West and the Dry Tortugas on Half Moon Shoal with 488 crew and passengers aboard. All were registered missing without trace. She sailed a regular route between Spain and Puerto Rico, Cuba and the Gulf Coast of the United States. The hurricane hit Havana on September 08, before *Valbanera* reached the port. She was unable to enter the harbour and signalled that she would move away from the shore and ride out the storm.

Kurt and Dan knew that a storm was coming. Having spent so many years at sea forever watching the weather their instincts had never failed them. The first tropical cyclone warning prompted by the United States Weather Bureau was a storm warning that came on Monday September 8th. It was issued for areas along the Florida coast from Jupiter on the east coast to Fort Myers on the west coast with the storm already a hurricane over the Bahamas.

Mary Star of the Sea had been contracted to take a family group of six wealthy tourists and business people to Cuba. The arrangements had been planned many months beforehand. September 7th, 1919 was a Sunday, a day when Kurt and Dan always agreed to stay home, attend church and spend the remainder of their day with their young families.

However, Mr. Roberto, a particularly wealthy, extremely successful, well-connected businessman and Edward, his right-hand man, together with Mr. Roberto's immediate family planned to head to Cuba to celebrate his 60th birthday. Mr. Roberto offered a huge sum of money to cover the inconvenience of sailing on a Sunday. It was a considerable temptation and hard to pass over. Dan and Kurt finally agreed to take him up on his request. The party planned to stay at Havana's oldest hotel, The Inglaterra. The hotel management was in the process of organizing a large reception with dancing and entertainment for the group on the evening of Tuesday September 9th. Several Cuban businessmen, dignitaries and socialites had been invited. Mr. Roberto and his group insisted that they made the crossing on Sunday because the businessman had important business appointments early on Monday in Havana. He planned to take Flagler's Overseas Railroad from Miami on Saturday September 6th, stay in Key West for the night and sail to Cuba on the 7th.

In 1915 a ferry service had been inaugurated connecting Havana to Key West. P&O freight car ferries could hold 26 large Flagler railroad freight cars. Of course, the wealthy businessman knew of this service but he disliked the idea of a large ship. He was somewhat superstitious and had heard nothing but good reports about Kurt and Dan's very small, discreet private ferry service aboard *Mary Star of the Sea*. The party was instructed to gather on the dock with their luggage early on Sunday morning just as the sun rose for the 90-mile crossing. *Mary Star of the Sea* averaged around 9 knots per hour so the crossing would take at least 10 hours depending upon the maritime conditions. Kurt had never felt good about this business transaction. He and Dan argued endlessly over the proposal before finally agreeing. Kurt's family meant more to him than the money on the table but both brothers knew that such a large, unexpected sum would enable them to purchase luxuries that the two brothers could only dream about. In the end it was the money that persuaded Kurt. It tempted both young men and won their heated arguments.

On Saturday night Kurt's beloved grandfather intervened and appeared in his dreams. Since the old man's passing in 1905 Kurt had never really felt the closeness of his presence. Neither had he a sense that his grandfather had ever visited before in a dream. However, this particular night the old man appeared in his dream standing on the quayside next to *Mary Star of the Sea*. He was shaking his head and pointing up to the sky where storm clouds were gathering. He looked Kurt in the eye and simply said, "Kurt stay home! She won't be returning to the dock if you set sail for Cuba. Mark my word boy, stay on shore, tie her up good and tight and keep your family safe, the big storm is coming." Kurt woke up with a start. The dream had been so vivid then he smelt a whiff of tobacco in the bedroom. It was such a familiar smell. Fondly he remembered his grandfather puffing away on his old clay pipe as he'd sat on his knee in his younger years. When Kurt smelt the tobacco, he knew grandfather had come to warn him. He didn't sleep well for the rest of the night. He tossed and turned anxiously thinking how he could possibly turn the party away and tell them that there would be no passage to Cuba on Sunday. "What on earth will Dan say?" Kurt kept asking himself.

Kurt didn't feel good at all. When he finally climbed out of bed his nerves were on edge, never before in his whole life had he felt this anxious. The sun was just coming up; his young family still slept as he left home and made his way hurriedly towards the harbour. His heart felt heavy and was pounding away in his chest. A fresh wind was blowing but the sun was shining. Dan was already aboard taking on provisions for the crossing and checking the engine. Kurt stepped aboard and confronted his brother. A fierce argument ensured. "Kurt, you're crazy, we can't just back out, there's so much money on the table. This businessman is influential he could see to it that our livelihood is taken away from us. He's not the sort of man that will take no for an answer! Yes, I think some bad weather is coming but it looks fine today and if we get going quickly, we'll be in Havana by this evening. We can take shelter in the harbour if there's a storm."

The wealthy party arrived a few minutes later, two cars from their fancy Key West hotel had brought them to the dock and a bellboy was busily unloading their luggage. Kurt felt desperate. How could he possibly tell them that the crossing wouldn't be going ahead? He sat slumped on one of the benches with his hands covering his head desperately praying for guidance. Grandfather came to his rescue once again. He felt a heavy hand on his shoulder; he smelt a whiff of tobacco once again and heard his gentle but firm voice whispering in his ear. "Kurt, find the courage to say no. If *Mary Star of the Sea* leaves this dock today mark my word she will not return. You and Dan will not return. A catastrophic storm is coming; surely you know that lives are worth more than all this money. Stand up for your convictions. You can't outrun this storm, stay home." Dan shook Kurt, "Get up the party are here, it's time to leave." Then he turned around and caught a whiff of his grandfather's tobacco and stopped in his tracks. Kurt jumped to his feet and simply said, "Today we stay home because a catastrophic storm is coming."

Mr. Roberto was not used to being told what to do. He simply laughed when Kurt told him that a catastrophic storm was coming and that *Mary Star of the Sea* would not be making the crossing to Cuba today. Then he became very angry and started to make threats. Kurt bravely stood his ground. He felt grandfather's firm, steadying hand upon his shoulder as he begun to speak with authority. "Dan and I are experienced boatmen; we know these waters and we know the weather. We cannot afford to get caught on the open sea unable to out run a severe storm. Lives may be lost. Return to your hotel and we'll take you as soon as we know that it will be safe to do so." By this time the businessman was red in the face and shaking. He bellowed to the drivers of the two cars and the bellboy to reload their luggage. He turned to Kurt and Dan shaking his head and pointing his finger. "You haven't heard the last of this! You're in trouble, nobody ever tells me what to do!"

Sister Louis Gabriel of the sisters of the Holy Names of Jesus and Mary had arrived in Key West in late August of 1897 and since her arrival she'd experienced and survived three major hurricanes. Sister witnessed so much devastation, heartache and loss over her years in Key West that she felt the coral island desperately needed to be protected from future storms. Her passion instigated the building of the *Hurricane Grotto* to the south of *The Basilica of Mary, Star of the Sea* to seek the protection of Our Blessed Mother Mary. *The Hurricane Grotto* containing statues of Our Lady of Lourdes and Bernadette was finished and dedicated on May 25th, 1922. Sister Gabriel is said to have said at its dedication,

> *"As long as the grotto stands Key West will never again experience the full brunt of a hurricane."*

George, Elsie, Kurt, Dan and their families were all present at that 1922 dedication. As members of the church congregation and seafarers they knew only too well the fragility of their home. A sudden change in the idyllic, balmy tropical weather could herald disastrous consequences. They all knew of friends and neighbours who'd lost their homes and for some, their lives. This community of fishermen and boat people were tight knit. They all depended upon the sea for income in one way or another. They understood and were thankful for the many blessings that their maritime home gave them. However, they all understood and feared the darker side of their existence when they were all truly at the mercy of Mother Nature's wrath. George, Kurt, Dan and the family understood more than most the beneficent protection that *Mary Star of the Sea* bestowed.

At that dedication Kurt reflected back to that fateful day in early September 1919 when, with his deceased grandfather's help, he'd stood his ground and faced a very angry man. He shuddered and wondered what would have happened if they had agreed and put out to sea that day. Kurt muttered under his breath, "Grandfather was right, he saved our lives, we would not have returned." Then he recalled the visit they received from Mr. Roberto when the hurricane was finally over. The business man was extremely humble, he thanked them for standing up to him, he told them he had learnt a powerful life lesson. Then he produced a wad of notes thrusting them into Kurt's hand and simply saying, "A gift from my family to yours. Spend it as you please. You and your brother saved my life and the lives of my loved ones. Thank you."

The money came in useful as some repairs were necessary after the devastating hurricane of 1919 but there was plenty left over. Over the next few years Kurt and Dan were able to take their families on vacation. They travelled on The Overseas Railroad and visited other towns in mainland Florida, places they'd only read about in the newspapers. One year they took a special family trip on the train all the way to New York. Before he passed away old Alfred had told them about his family up in Buffalo, New York so they looked them up and were escorted to Niagara Falls for a wonderful sightseeing opportunity. The Overseas Railroad brought thousands of visitors to Key West from Miami and many of these visitors took the steamers over to Cuba. Business was also brisk for Kurt and Dan; they enjoyed a good standard of living as they continued to run their small private ferry service back and forth to Cuba. During prohibition, returning baggage labelled *clothing* was often filled with bottles of alcohol. When there were no passengers, they cast their trawling nets and *Mary Star of the Sea* brought in good catches that were sold at the local market.

However, life was not so good for many other Key West residents because by 1934, the Great Depression had devastated the city. The city government defaulted on more than $5,000,000 of bonded debt. 80% of the population needed some sort of government financial assistance. City services had become pretty much non-existent because employees went without pay for weeks at a time. The city could no longer afford a police, fire or sanitation service. Jobs were also non-existent. At one time the lucrative cigar manufacturing industry that had employed so many and had made Key West the wealthiest city in Florida had sadly declined. By 1931 all the large cigar factories in Key West had closed down. Over fishing for sponges, the use of heavy boots and diving suits and a deadly sponge fungus meant that sponge fishing had relocated to mainland Florida and Tarpon Springs. The once thriving pineapple canning industry collapsed because there were higher tariffs on pineapples. The island's army base had been reduced, the naval base abandoned and the coast guard's district headquarters removed. The city was no longer a port of call for the Mallory Steamship Lines' passenger ships and there was a reduction of freight from Cuba to Key West. More than 6,000 residents had already moved away in search of a living elsewhere. Those who remained were barely getting by.

It was a time of great reflection for Kurt and Dan and gratitude for their own good fortune. The brothers had been truly blessed with a reliable boat and their families were reasonably comfortable. However, they were quick to share what they had and to help friends and neighbours in need. More than half of their catch was always donated to the church soup kitchen. Small local fish were boiled with key limes, onions, green peppers and seasonings and served over grits; a nutritious and palatable meal resulted. The situation became so bad that local officials even considered relocating the entire population of this coral island at the end of America to Tampa. Julius F. Stone Jr. north-eastern director of the Federal Emergency Relief Administration came to town to set about rectifying the economic situation. The city was in a dire financial crisis and they had to quickly implement an effective economic plan to save the Key West community.

Several programs were initiated to help remaining residents obtain employment and instil pride. Julius Stone organized the Key West Work Corps, consisting of 4,000 members. They cleaned up the city, painted and remodelled buildings and planted thousands of coconut palms along the streets of Key West. The tree planting provided employment but also added to the tropical ambience. Photographs depicted a tempting tropical paradise. The city desperately needed to attract tourists from the north as tourist dollars would be the lifeblood, they required to enable the community to sustain itself. Thankfully they reached their goal; during the winter of 1934 40,000 tourists were attracted to the city.

Kurt was forty-five years old when the Labor Day hurricane of September 2nd, 1935 hit. It has often been dubbed The Storm of The

Century affecting The Bahamas, Florida Keys, southwest and north Florida. It was the most intense Atlantic hurricane to make landfall on record in terms of both pressure and wind speed. In modern terms labelled as a category 5 hurricane. It is said to have cleared every tree and building off Matecumbe Key. People caught in the open were blasted by sand with such force that it stripped away their clothing! The storm killed somewhere between 400 - 600 people and caused estimated damage amounting to one hundred million dollars. Sister Louis Gabriel's *Hurricane Grotto* protected Key West from the full brunt of the storm, thankfully only minimal damage occurred in the city. However, there were absolutely devastating consequences further north in the Upper Florida Keys. It devastated Long Key and adjacent areas.

This hurricane ended Henry Flagler's railroad dream. Wind gusts of 150 - 200 miles per hour and 18 - 20-foot tides at Islamorada swept away buildings and 35 miles of railroad track, and even most of the rescue train sent to evacuate residents. 259 World War 1 veterans living in three Civilian Conservation Corps camps while they worked on building the new Overseas Highway died because their rescue train arrived too late. Only a handful of people survived. The author Ernest Hemingway visited the Keys after the storm and wrote a scathing magazine article critical of the rescue efforts titled, "Who killed the Vets?"

Everyone was unsettled after that devastating hurricane. It was going to cost far too much money to rebuild the damaged railroad so it was decided to abandon the project. State and Federal money was used to purchase the railroad's right-of-way and bridges. Expansion of the Overseas Highway to Key West began in earnest. Of course, the Great Depression had already devastated Key West, so the loss of Flagler's railroad was an extra blow. Everyone began to look forward to the eventual completion of the new highway.

It took Kurt and Dan a couple of years to finally make a momentous family decision. Actually, it was George's death in early January of

1936, followed by their mother Elsie only a few months later that prompted them to finally made up their minds. The two brothers and their respective families decided it was time to reinvent their lives once again and carve out a new beginning. On his deathbed George simply said, "Key West has served our family well. Soon I'll join all our relatives in the graveyard; I think it won't be long before Elsie follows along too. It's been our tropical paradise, but on occasion it's been a living hell for all of us. Who knows what the future will bring? Perhaps there will be more hurricanes, perhaps there will be even more devastation. Life here is so uncertain. I know you boys have enjoyed your vacation travels up north. I've heard that the fishing up in Maine is particularly good and we've distant relatives who settled there a long time ago and work in a boatbuilding yard. That state is so far up north that it has never experienced the wrath of a hurricane. When Elsie and I finally pass on please don't feel that you have to remain here at the end of America. The next generation may thank you for moving on and starting again up north where there's so much more opportunity for my grandchildren. It may be the best decision that you will ever make. Give it some serious thought and know that if you decide to leave our little coral island paradise that you have my blessing and your mother's too."

With Elsie's passing the family decided it was also their time to leave. Preparations were made to start the long journey north to Portland, Maine in early May when the weather was generally reasonably stable. Relatives would be waiting for their arrival and would help to get them settled. It would take *Mary Star of the Sea* about four weeks of continuous navigation depending upon good local weather conditions. They planned to load up the whole family and drop their wives and Kurt's daughters off in Miami so that they could continue the journey north by train. Kurt, Dan and his two sons would man their trusty boat and continue their long voyage northwards. Kurt and Dan put their small cottages up for sale. They'd quickly cleared their parent's family home and a neighbour had already agreed to purchase the brightly painted clapboard bungalow.

There was much to do as they prepared to say goodbye to their island paradise. Of course, Kurt had mixed feelings. The future was somewhat daunting but his father was right there would be much more opportunity in Portland and certainly better prospects for his daughters who were now beautiful young ladies. They would always sleep well at night because living in fear of the hurricane season would be a thing of the past. No more wondering if and when the next big storm would hit and if they would survive.

In the loft of their little bungalow Kurt discovered a large cardboard box and was pleasantly surprised to find his old three-pronged sponge fishing pole and a bag of sponges. Kurt sat quietly with his pole for a long time and as he gently fingered the old wood, he reflected upon the fond memories of his younger days out on the water with his grandfather. As he reflected, he sensed his grandfather's heavy hand upon his shoulder and heard him whisper in his ear, "Kurt, it's time to move on and start again. Leave the sponge pole here it belongs in Key West and our past. It's time to forge ahead and make some new memories with your family in another place. Always know that you have my blessing and know that wherever you are I won't be far away. Just ask if you ever need my help."

The little bungalow was eventually sold and over the years there were many owners. Lydia purchased it as a holiday home in the 1990's and lived there until her death in early 2021. Then the enterprising young couple from New York who bought the cottage in the summer had grand plans to renovate their investment property and turn it into a lucrative Airbnb holiday rental. Kurt's cardboard box was discovered in the loft and without much thought the young man from New York left it on the doorstep of St. Eustace thinking that the vintage shop might be interested. Curiously some strange unseen force stopped him at the very last minute from tossing it onto the bonfire that he'd built at the end of the little garden.

Desmond opened his eyes and looked down lovingly upon the old wooden pole and the handful of dried sponges. "That's quite a story," he muttered to Henry who'd crept silently onto his velvet cushion and sat patiently beside him. Later in the day when the house was quiet Desmond shared his story with Harriet and Bella. Even Linda, who was usually busy doing something or other in the sewing room, sat down with a cup of tea and a piece of Ruth's divine chocolate cake and listened intently. Harriet smiled and said, "Desmond, those of us who have lived here for so long always stop by Sister Louis Gabriel's *Hurricane Grotto* before a storm to pray. Many people gather there especially when there's a hurricane warning. Candles are lit and people pray and thank the Lord because Key West has never taken a direct hit since that grotto was established. In September 2017 when Hurricane Irma, a category 4 storm, hit the Keys and caused major damage Key West was spared. In fact, our city has always been spared since *The Hurricane Grotto* was established because Mother Mary continues to keep her beneficent, watchful eye over this little coral island at the end of America!"

Bella continued the conversation by making an interesting observation about the sponges. "Those sponges have all kinds of uses, today we tend to use synthetic ones but I remember back in the late 1950's my little Florence was always so sick, pale and lethargic and it was those sponges that saved her life!" Desmond patted the old lady on the arm and said, "How so, Bella?" The old woman sat back and smiled, "She was my third child and always the sickly one. She was weak, her glands were swollen and her chest was forever bad. The doctor said she had asthma. She had many colds, sore throats, ear infections and those terrible coughs. Florence was always worse when it got colder and at night. She would gasp for air. She had such trouble breathing. I always saw this frightened look on her face because she seemed to be suffocating. She sounded like a dog continually barking. Her cough was dry, harsh and loud. I would sit her up in bed and boil the kettle. I would try to have her inhale the steam. Hot drinks were helpful too. Well, one night shortly after she turned three years old, we nearly lost her. Her breathing was so bad that night and the steam didn't seem to help at all. It was late but my husband ran out for the doctor. I sat praying that he could help because in the past he had little to offer. That night was different because he brought a friend, another doctor, who was visiting. I was told that he was a homeopathic doctor and that his strange little white pills might possibly help my poor Florence. He put some little white pills under her tongue and within a short space of time her cough settled down and she began to breathe more normally. It was truly a miracle. He left us a little bottle so that if an episode ever happened again, we could give her the pills. I asked what was in the pills and he told me that they were made from roasted sponges! I was amazed because it was sponges that had brought Key West fame and fortune in the past! We used those pills several times as Florence grew and they always helped. In the end she became much stronger and eventually seemed to grow out of her susceptibility to asthma. She's in her sixties now with a family of her own and lots of grandchildren. She has a little box of homeopathic remedies and always helps us with them if we're feeling unwell. I call them the little white miracle pills!"

Desmond sat back and smiled. "Thank you, ladies, for sharing. I'm not sure what we can do with the sponge pole and these sponges but I'm sure that Madam Popoff will have something to say about that. I'm going to try and read about this medicine called homeopathy. Our ocean has so much to offer. Mother Nature can take away but she's also the giver of life and who would ever have thought that the humble sponge has such healing properties and the ability to save lives!" It was getting late and time to close up St. Eustace for the night. Cora had stopped by to collect Linda. Pastor Joe arrived with the old yellow church bus for Harriet and Bella and as Desmond locked up, he muttered to himself, "Yet another interesting and successful day in paradise."

Thanksgiving

Maria Popoff was delighted when Desmond shared his story of the sponge pole. She ran her fingers lovingly down the old wooden pole and smiled. "That's quite a story and how grateful the people of Key West must be for Sister Louis Gabriel's *Hurricane Grotto*! We have many weeks to prepare St. Eustace for The Thanksgiving Holiday Desmond. We all have much to be thankful for and I want our community to do something special for the holiday. Perhaps you'll give it some thought." Desmond quietly muttered to himself, "That's a very tall order!"

However, Halloween was a more pressing issue and on everyone's mind. Cora was spending more time at St. Eustace helping out and generously offered to decorate for this holiday weekend. Maria suggested that everyone in the St. Eustace community wore a costume on October 31st and that the house would be open in the early evening to greet any children who would be making the rounds. Everyone had agreed upon homemade cookies and lemonade.

Cora was so very grateful that her Linda seemed to have settled down. Linda absolutely loved being in the old house. She happily cleaned and polished everything in sight. When Bella taught her how to cut around the tissue paper patterns pinned to beautiful brightly coloured fabric she couldn't wait to get up in the morning. Her days of aimless restlessness were over. Linda had become so much more focused and purposeful. She dressed herself, helped Cora make breakfast and couldn't wait to get out of the house and wander down the road to her second home. The St. Eustace community had taken Linda under their wing. Every one watched out for her and she was blossoming before their eyes. She was still mute but one particular day when she thought no one was looking Ruth observed her cuddling and muttering away to Henry.

Cora was looking so much better too, knowing that her Linda was happy, gainfully employed and watched over by many caring eyes. For the first time since Linda had been a small child Cora felt that the stressful burden of responsibility had been lifted from her weary shoulders. She woke each day feeling light hearted and joyful. The enormous black cloud that had descended upon her life and home had dissipated. She was now able to get out and about, meeting old friends for coffee, working out at the gym and swimming in the ocean. As Cora's energy and zest for life returned, she began to feel like a young woman once more and eager to fully participate in life.

As Halloween approached, she made several trips to the pumpkin patch stand out on Highway 1 and loaded up her car with bright orange pumpkins of various sizes. Cousin Rollo and Fred took charge and along with several men who were now regular visitors to the St. Eustace garage community they spent many hours happily carving out Halloween lanterns. These would be lit by candles, placed around the wrap around porch and out by the front gates, then down the long driveway towards the big house on October 31st.

Ruth got busy in the kitchen and with Cora and Linda's help they baked hundreds of Halloween cookies. Harriet and Bella invited the women's prayer group from church over for afternoon tea on October 28th. Following tea and a slice of Ruth's wonderful chocolate cake they donned aprons and busily decorated the cookies with coloured icing and little sweet decorations. There was animated discussion about costumes amongst those who planned to be at St. Eustace on Halloween. Desmond really liked the idea of a Star Wars Theme. He rather thought that he might make a great Han Solo. Cora thought that Linda would look good as Princess Leia. Cora, with her short-cropped hair, decided upon Luke Skywalker. Fred offered to dress up as Chewbacca, Cousin Rollo decided upon Obi - Wan Kenobi and Ruth offered to dress up as Darth Vader.

All in all, the Halloween party atmosphere placed St. Eustace well and truly on the map! Local children enjoyed wandering up the long driveway lit by carefully carved magical lanterns glowing in the dark. Excited groups of children loved the home baked cookies and lemonade offered up by their favourite Star Wars characters. Cora's Linda was in her element she enjoyed her Princess Leia costume so much that she insisted upon wearing it around the house every day for the next two weeks!

After the excitement of Halloween Desmond immediately began to direct his focus upon a plan for Thanksgiving. He discovered that there were many lonely Key West residents. Apparently, a number of the locals had lost their loved ones to Covid. After much thought Desmond decided upon a holiday luncheon party for anyone who would be on their own and without family on Thanksgiving Day. He placed an advert in several local papers and magazines and quickly received 50 responses. After calling a house meeting everyone began to plan in earnest. Obviously, the traditional Thanksgiving turkeys would be a major cost incurred by the St. Eustace budget. Cora graciously agreed to visit some of the farm to table shops and offered to purchase all the vegetables needed for the tables. Ruth volunteered to stay late in the evenings and bake a number of pumpkin and pecan pies. Harriet and Bella offered to run up a number of colourful tablecloths and matching napkins. Recently two large bolts of cotton fabric had been left on the St. Eustace doorstep. They featured a fall design with lots of trees, turning leaves, berries and woodland animals. Cousin Rollo smiled, "Those new tablecloths will be a timely reminder and so much a part of what St. Eustace is all about. A loving testament to Dick and Dolly's cherished son, David, who loved the woodlands so much." Harriet smiled, "Linda can help with the cutting out of the cloth, this will keep her busy for the next few days!" Pastor Joe, who had become a regular visitor at the house, volunteered to bring the church choir to sing some thanksgiving songs after the meal when they planned to serve coffee and homemade sweets. Maria had befriended one of the bar keepers down near the harbour and he offered to bring his Caribbean steel calypso band over for a one-hour concert following on from Pastor Joe's choir.

St. Eustace was quickly gathering a reputation for hospitality, a place where everyone could feel welcome. The coffee shop had become a hive of activity pulling in the early morning crowd. The soup kitchen was always busy over the lunchtime period. The patio had become a gathering place for the city's homeless as the community's reputation for freshly baked bread, cheese and hot, hearty vegetable soup had spread far and wide. A quick turn around after lunch readied the patio and elegant dining room for afternoon tea. Ruth's home-made scones and special chocolate cake had very quickly gained a reputation and bookings for table reservations were becoming difficult to come by as more and more elderly snow birds liked to come and socialize in the afternoon hours. Betty's close friend Julie had been looking for a new job and given St. Eustace's growing popularity Maria decided to engage her help too.

By the time that Thanksgiving eve actually came around everyone was totally exhausted. St. Eustace was finally ready to welcome 50 excited guests for the luncheon party the next day. Ruth, Betty, Julie, Cora, and Linda had baked the pies and homemade sweets and prepared the vegetables. Ruth, along with Fred's help, was going to come in very early to cook the turkeys. The patio and dining room were all set up. Harriet, Bella and Linda had completed a great job creating the new tablecloths and matching napkins. Cora, Fred and Cousin Rollo had finished decorating the house and patio with beautiful fall floral displays. Several of the men who'd been working together on the old cars out in the garages had assembled a large marquee in the grounds ready for the afternoon concert. Over 50 chairs, lent by one of the large downtown hotels, were set in place.

Maria asked everyone to join her in the sewing room at 6pm for tea and a slice of chocolate cake. As they gathered around the large table Maria faced the weary group. She smiled and said, "I'm so very happy to be here in Key West, the end of the road. Thanks to you all we've created a special place, a community, a refuge, a place to gather and share. For some it's a place to heal and for many it's a place to reflect and give thanks." Turning to Desmond she said, "Everybody and everything that crosses our threshold has a special story to tell. Forgotten treasures, hidden away, are coming to light and sharing their stories too. Everyone experiences ups and downs in life, the good and the bad times. However, it's about how we set our compass and navigate our lives and, in the end, only three things matter. *How much you loved, how gently you lived and how gracefully you let go of things not meant for you."* Much to everyone's surprise Maria suddenly placed the long wooden sponge pole upon the table together with a handful of sponges. "Most of you have heard Desmond's lovely story. I want you all to think about how we can celebrate this treasure that made its way to our door. I'm open to suggestions. Happy Thanksgiving everyone and thank you!"

Gingerbread Houses

With the successful Thanksgiving celebrations over, Christmas 2021 was looming closely upon the horizon. There were a couple of beautiful pine trees growing in the grounds of St. Eustace and Fred suggested that they would look wonderful dressed up for the season in colourful lights and outdoor baubles. Everyone agreed so the next day Fred and Cousin Rollo visited Strunk Ace Hardware on Eaton Street adjacent to the Naval Air Station. For generations family run Strunk Hardware has served the community at the end of the road. It's a veritable Aladdin's cavern and one of those places that seemingly sells everything that one could possibly imagine and more! Watching Cousin Rollo, Fred and Desmond out in the gardens decorating the majestic pines set Cora thinking about the interior of the grand house.

Harriet and Bella were busy as usual in the sewing room but Cora's offer of an outing to Strunk's and a nice luncheon afterwards at a fancy Key West restaurant was hard to pass up. Cora helped the two elderly ladies into her SUV and they set off for their very own adventure. Strunk's is one of those magical places where one can spend hours browsing but Cora helped to keep everyone focused. As they stood patiently in line to purchase garlands of fir and baubles Harriet suddenly noticed the gingerbread kits. "Cora, I think it would be lovely if we offered a gingerbread house competition. We could talk to the social services folk and invite some of the at risk children to visit St. Eustace and participate. We could even arrange a Christmas party for the children afterwards and Cousin Rollo would make a wonderful Santa Claus!" Cora knew there and then that this was a really lovely suggestion and she made the snap decision to use her own money to purchase 13 kits. She wasn't sure why 13 came to mind but it seemed important. Helping out at St. Eustace and being around Maria Popoff for some time now had taught Cora many things, the most important being to trust one's own gut feelings.

Maria Popoff was delighted when the excited ladies eventually returned to St. Eustace and shared their ideas. Later that afternoon Maria summoned everyone to the sewing room for a house discussion. Pastor Joe had already dropped by in the old yellow school bus to pick up Harriet and Bella but Maria insisted that he joined their meeting. Over tea and chocolate cake it was agreed that the afternoon of Sunday December 19th would be perfect as it gave them all plenty of time to plan. Pastor Joe knew many of the social services folk and he agreed to talk with them. They needed to identify 13 at risk children who would really benefit from spending an afternoon at St. Eustace. Ruth agreed to bake for their Christmas party and would ask Betty and Julie to help out on the big day. Cousin Rollo, after some persuasion, agreed to hire a Santa Claus costume and procure 13 gifts. Fred thought that Linda would make a great elf because she loved to dress up and her busy hands would be a great help to Santa!

Everyone was getting into the Christmas spirit. Fred and Desmond along with Cora, Linda and Ruth spent the best part of Thursday December 2nd decorating the large Christmas tree that Cousin Rollo brought home from Strunk's Hardware. The tantalizing aroma of fresh pine needles wafted through the hall of the grand house and customers who came to browse the vintage shop and visit the café often stopped by to admire the enormous tree gracing the hall with its sparkling fairy lights and shiny silver and pale blue baubles. Linda had recently taken an interest in mermaids. She'd seen a picture in a children's book and was fixated upon the magical creatures. Cora remembered seeing mermaid ornaments down on Mallory Square in the tourist shops so she purchased a box full of the little ornaments and Linda, together with Fred's help, excitedly hung them on the tree. When she was particularly tired St. Eustace folk noticed that she liked to sit under the enormous Christmas tree adorned with lights and mermaids. It seemed to be Linda's calming, peaceful place.

It was in the all the hub bub and excitement of the Christmas festivities that Brenda walked through the door of St. Eustace. She seemed to be somewhat in a daze and carried a large suitcase. Desmond was the first to notice her. The vintage shop was busy and he was checking out some purchases but she immediately caught his eye because there was something strange about this middle-aged lady that just didn't seem right. Her expensive looking clothes didn't match, she was wearing odd shoes and her dyed blonde hair needed a good comb. Maria also made a sudden, unexpected appearance and turning to Desmond she simply said, "Desmond leave her to me." Desmond looked on as Maria gently took the strange woman's hand and discreetly led her back through the hall steering her into the sewing room. Today the room was empty because Harriet and Bella were participating in the church Christmas outing. Pastor Joe had planned a picnic luncheon on Southern Point Beach for the women's prayer group. Maria beckoned Brenda to sit down on the large comfy armchair in the corner of the room and she perched herself on the end of the chaise longue. Maria reached out her hand intuitively and gently put Brenda's neatly manicured fingers, sporting luscious red polish, into the palm of her own wrinkled hands. The two women looked into each other's eyes then Brenda began to speak in slow, slurred monotones.

"I've brought a case full of clothes for the shop full of pretty things that I used to wear a long time ago. I'm sorting things out because it won't be long before I'm gone." Brenda suddenly began to sob, salty tears cascaded down her face, her body began to shake and she clasped her hands together in anguish. Maria sat still, remained present and eventually took her hands again and patiently waited for Brenda to speak once more. After some time, she sighed and said, "I've got dementia. The doctor says that it'll only get worse and eventually I'll have to go into some sort of care home. He says there's nothing that can be done. I'm sorting things out while I still can. I'm only fifty years old. Some days I can't remember where I live but today when I woke up, I heard a strange voice in my bedroom telling me to bring clothes here. I think it was yesterday that I saw a story about this place in a magazine. I can't even remember how I got here today! I think that I came in a taxi, maybe I gave the driver the magazine and he knew about this place." Maria smiled and gently said, "Brenda welcome and thank you for the clothes. If you'll let us, we'll try and help you to recover some of your health and be as well as you can be. Can you please tell me more about your life or as much as you can remember right now?"

There was a long silence but Maria remained silent and patiently held Brenda's delicate hands. More sobbing ensued but eventually Brenda dried her eyes and told her story. "I grew up in Pittsburgh. My father worked in a steel mill. We lived beside a busy highway. I remember there was lots of traffic and so much noise practically all the time. I especially remember the traffic fumes because they really irritated my lungs. The doctor diagnosed asthma. I'd such a difficult time in school because academic work just wasn't for me but upon graduation, I gained a place at cosmetology school. I absolutely loved to do peoples hair, their make-up and their nails. I've always been good with my hands and really enjoyed helping people to look good. I love pretty clothes too, all sorts of girly things! There are some cute outfits in the suitcase that I've here with me right now!

When I married my husband, who happens to be fifteen years older than me, was offered a good job in Mexico City so we relocated there. It was also noisy and polluted just like the place where I'd grown up but thinking about that now it may have been even worse. Certainly, my asthma flared up and I had to rely upon inhalers all the time. Of course, we wanted children but that never happened. No children meant that we had plenty of money. There was time to party and eat out at fancy restaurants. For years I drank far too much, mainly gin and tonics, fancy tequila cocktails and sparkling white wine. It really was an easy way to drown my sorrows, because when I'd had too much to drink, I didn't have to worry that we had no family of our own. Also, all the alcohol made it so much easier for me to accept that my husband had a roving eye. I'm sure that he had a few affairs while we lived in that awful city. To be honest I was numb and drunk a lot of the time. Eventually I began to experience very bad headaches and I was often sick. The doctor told me to quit the drinking so I switched to Coca-Cola instead.

My husband retired six months ago and told me several years ago that he'd always wanted to live in Key West. He'd an old uncle who lived here and he remembered idyllic childhood school vacations down on the Florida Keys helping his uncle out on his sport fishing boat. We moved here a few months ago and live in a nice house. I think that it might be located on Eaton Street. Some days I do remember and some days it seems as if everything is a complete mystery. My husband has bought a sport fishing boat. He keeps it in the harbour but he's gone much of the time. He's made new friends. I'm stuck at home all alone. There's no one that I know here in Key West. I'd noticed a few years ago that my memory wasn't so good. I would write myself notes and lists to avoid embarrassment. The girls who worked with me in the hair salon in Mexico City would have to remind me of things. I think that they took turns to watch out for me and cover up my mistakes. I know that I can't get a job here because my mind isn't working well at all. I'm lonely and to be perfectly honest I'm very frightened, terrified even! I don't know what to do. The doctor says there's really not much he can do, maybe some pills to slow things down. This is terrible, I'm only fifty years old." Brenda started to sob once again.

Maria sat with her in silence then after some time passed, she quietly whispered, "Brenda, if you manage to get better and recover your memory what will you do with the rest of your life? What sort of future can you imagine? How will you pass the remainder of your days? What gifts will you share for the greater good if you're given a second chance at life?" Brenda was taken by surprise, she'd been made to believe that she had no future, that she would be confined to some sort of home where she would spend what time she had left and that it wouldn't be very pleasant at all.

Brenda looked the curious wizened, roly-poly woman in the eye and said, "I've always enjoyed helping people. I'm clever at making them look nice so that they feel good about themselves. I've a good eye for colour, dresses and hair styles. People like to talk to hairdressers. Customers often confide their problems and share the secrets of their heart. I've always been a good listener. That's my gift, I care. My regular customers in Mexico City always appreciated me being there for them and the advice that I was sometimes able to offer. I even learnt to speak Spanish! The girls that I worked with liked me. I think that's why they looked out for me when they began to realize that I wasn't well."

Maria smiled and said, "Brenda, today you were led to the right place. St. Eustace is a caring community. You'll find love, friendship and support her. You'll have to make a lot of changes and be open to try new things to help get your mind and your body healthier. If you truly want to recover your health then you'll have to dive right in and make a mammoth effort. You need to detoxify from all the pollution you've been exposed to over the years and all that alcohol! You'll have to follow a special diet, give up sugar and especially all that Coca-Cola. You may have to change all of your cleaning and personal care products, exercise, be open to herbs, flower essences and homeopathic remedies. There's much that can be done to help you Brenda but you have to be totally committed. Is this what you want and are prepared to work towards?"

A long awkward silence followed then Brenda finally spoke, "I'm ready. I don't want to die. I'm far too young. Some unseen force pushed me here today and I'm thankful for that. I do believe that I'm ready to listen, follow guidance and make big changes." Maria sighed with relief knowing full well that when someone is on their right path and is willing to commit then the universe puts all kinds of people and things on their path to help facilitate the best possible outcome. Maria suggested to Brenda that she ask Cora to bring her SUV around to the front of the grand house and that they both take her home. Brenda allowed Maria to look inside her handbag to find her address. Eaton Street was nearby so after a short car ride she even allowed Maria and Cora to come into her home and take a look around so that they could offer immediate suggestions regarding lifestyle changes. There was much that needed to change. It was obvious that Brenda would require a great deal of education and support but the biggest obstacle was removed when Brenda declared that she was ready and willing to do the work.

The next day Maria requested that everyone participate in another house meeting after the vintage shop and porch café closed. St. Eustace folk gathered around the large oak table in the sewing room. Linda busied herself bringing pots of tea and the special chocolate cake. Everyone was curious thinking that some sort of emergency concerning the Christmas party might have arisen. When everyone was settled Maria retold Brenda's story and explained her current predicament. Turning to all the anxious, concerned faces around the table Maria said, "St. Eustace is a caring, compassionate community and it's our duty to help Brenda as much as we possibly can. It really does take a village and right now she has no support. If it's possible for her to recover some of her health and brain function, she'll need our care and dedication. Cora and I've already identified many things in her home that need to change. We've made a very long list.

Firstly, kicking all the sugar and the Coca-Cola and absolutely no alcohol at all. Then switching to a plant based organic diet free from GMO's and pesticides. Ensuring that she eats real food that isn't cooked in a microwave or stored in a plastic container. Glass dishes are best. No processed and packaged foods that are full of chemicals and preservatives. No gluten or dairy. No high-fructose corn syrup and excitotoxins. These are chemical food additives such as aspartame and monosodium glutamate that over stimulate neurons in the brain and cause brain damage. She must get rid of the NutraSweet and Equal in her tea and coffee and the Splenda too. I noticed all of these products in her kitchen cupboard. No personal care products that have phthalates, parabens and formaldehyde. No nail polish or deodorant containing aluminium. There's a strong link between accumulations of aluminium and Alzheimer's. NO fluoride in her toothpaste.

Brenda has been exposed to a lot of pollution over her lifetime. It certainly didn't help living by a busy highway in Pittsburgh and then moving to Mexico City, one of the most polluted places in the world! It's highly likely that she'll have a lot of heavy metals that need to be detoxified. Her liver is probably in a sorry state from all that alcohol that she used to drown her sorrows. I'm going to talk with her husband

and see if he'll take her to see a really good functional medical doctor in town that has widespread training in holistic therapies such as homeopathy, acupuncture and cranial sacral therapy. He'll be able to run food allergy, parasite, mould and heavy metal tests so that Brenda and her husband have a clear idea of what she's allergic to and has to eliminate from her diet and how to detoxify her body in a safe way. It'll take a long time but I do believe that with the doctor's guidance and our continual support I'm sure that she'll make good progress. My long-term vision is to see the day when Brenda can come and work part time in the vintage shop. Obviously, that's when she's feeling much better and her brain is more functional! She'll be a great help to Desmond one day.

We all need to pray for and visualize a brighter future for Brenda and to that end I want us to create a rota of helpers whereby someone from St. Eustace visits her every day until she starts to feel better. More than anything she needs friends and people that she can talk to. She needs people to look out for her and ensure that she's taking her herbs, supplements and remedies and that she's following the best possible diet. She needs someone to take her for a long walk every day and ensure that she takes an Epsom salt foot bath to help pull out all those toxins. She can't walk this path alone but we can walk it with her and in the process we'll all learn how to be healthier."

The small group who had gathered around the oak table in the sewing room that evening had listened patiently. It felt like a tall order but everyone in the St. Eustace community had learnt that taking care of others, providing a place where everyone felt welcome and accepted was their priority and their mission. If it meant stepping up and lending a helping hand then so be it.

A rota was duly drawn up and as the weeks passed by everyone connected with St. Eustace lent a helping hand. It was the best Christmas gift that long suffering Brenda and her husband could ever have imagined. Sunday December 19th also proved to be a tremendous success. The social services had identified 12 at risk children who would really benefit from a special treat. However, at the very last minute eight-year-old David joined the group making it the anticipated number 13. He'd just been released from hospital. Tragically, young David been badly beaten by his step father whilst his mother had looked on. Social Services placed him in temporary foster care while the court was sorting out what was to be done about his future.

St. Eustace rang with the laughter of 13 excited children who enthusiastically made their ginger bread houses. Harriet and Bella had invited members of their women's prayer group to come by and help out. There were many sticky hands and a fun time was had by all. Cousin Rollo made a great Santa and Linda was beside herself with happiness all dressed up as his helper elf. Cora couldn't believe the transformation in her daughter knowing full well that they both had so much to be thankful for. In a quiet moment, amongst all the chaos and excitement of the party, she reflected upon Dick and Dolly's legacy to their beloved son and to the folk who'd made the grand old house come alive with the true spirit of Christmas.

The Margate Jetty

Be not inhospitable to strangers, lest they be angels in disguise

It was Sunday January 9th and a brand-new year. Poppy always viewed the New Year as a time to look forward with hope and expectation of better things to come. Thus far her life's path had taken an upward turn. Busy managing three vintage shops took up most of her time but she always found time to listen intently to those who showed up and asked for help. There were always so many broken pieces to mend. The New Year was an opportunity for new beginnings, a time to make personal promises; time to improve herself, to keep her own mirror polished. Eventually when her time came, she wished that the world would be in a better place because she had visited. Madam Popoff had taught her how to walk a path of goodness so that one day she would leave behind trails of beneficial and honourable legacies. Sadly, as 2022 dawned, the world was in a questionable, particularly alarming state of disarray. Whenever Poppy turned on the BBC news or read the papers there was always some kind of calamity. Violence across the globe appeared to be mirrored by violent, strange weather patterns causing destruction, chaos and heartbreak. Then there was the ever-present threat of the Corona virus and the ominous new variant, the dreaded highly infectious and aptly named Omicron. Masks, social distancing, booster jabs and personal safety briefings were the main topic of daily news broadcasts.

Today Poppy cycled with Jack the Lad down to the Margate seafront to watch the Blessing of the Seas. This is an annual event celebrated by the Greek Cypriot community. The event is the Greek Orthodox celebration at Epiphany marking the baptism of Christ. Margate was chosen for the honour in the mid - 20th century because there's a large community of Greek Cypriot residents. The archbishop and other church dignitaries from St. Michael of All Angels made a colourful scene, as the blessing ceremony got under way. This year there was no band or procession because of the ongoing Corona problem. Doves were released, prayers given and Theo Pantelli, a young lad from the local Greek community, braved the cold grey sea to retrieve an ornate, decorated cross cast into the murky waters by Archbishop Nikitas Loulias. Poppy reflected upon Archangel Michael, the great protector, and how his help was badly needed in these particularly troubled times.

Following the ceremony, she decided to make her way to King Street to open up for a few hours. Poppy hoped to catch the attention of stragglers from the crowd who'd gathered on the seafront for the ceremony. Locking up Dora, her trusty bicycle, by the cycle rack outside The Droit House Tourist Information Bureau she strode across the road with Jack the Lad towards Madam Popoff Vintage. Suddenly she stopped in her tracks. Much to her surprise someone had deposited a very large piece of what looked like driftwood on the doorstep. At first glance she felt annoyed because it almost blocked the entrance. It looked extremely cumbersome and seemed heavy but as she ran her hand over the rough wood, she immediately felt its energy and deep in her inner knowing she felt that this strange piece of wood had an important story to impart. Poppy unlocked the door, settled Jack the Lad upon his velvet cushion then crossed over the street to Olby's and asked if a couple of the fit young men working behind the bar could help her to shift the strange offering. After much huffing and puffing the heavy driftwood was laid to rest by a clothing rack displaying elegant vintage frocks and fancy white lace wedding gowns from the Edwardian and Victorian eras.

Opportunity to examine the strange driftwood didn't arise until much later in the day as Poppy had only just hung her coat and scarf up when several customers suddenly appeared on her doorstep. Business was brisk. The crowd gathering at the seafront for the blessing ceremony seemed to be in no hurry to head home. When the clock eventually struck four and the shop was finally empty Poppy locked the door and turned the sign to closed. She made herself a pot of tea and cut herself a slice of chocolate cake. There'd been no time for lunch, she was tired and in need of a boost of energy to help her cycle back home to Lookout Retreat with Jack the Lad. She pulled her chair over to the piece of driftwood and settled down to examine it further. Having drunk her tea and savoured a piece of cake she ran her delicate fingers over the wood, shut her eyes and drifted off to another time.

January 11-12[th]1978 saw a heavy gale and storm surge batter the southeast coast and destroyed what remained of the Margate jetty, changing the coastline forever. Actually, the jetty had closed to the public in 1976 due to safety reasons. The wood used in the construction was a South American hardwood from Guyana called Greenheart, used for its resilience in the marine environment and resistance to wood boring worms. It was often referred to as Ironwood given its incredible strength. However, the 1978 storm collapse was not due to the failure of the Greenheart. The crossbeams and foundations had failed. The collapse of the jetty saw many of the Greenheart timbers come ashore into the intertidal zone. Many were removed at the time; others remained buried.

Throughout the 1970's George, a successful middle-aged local businessman, anchored his pleasure craft in Margate harbour. At that time, it was a busy venue for small craft and fishing boats. Scattered throughout the harbour there remained the remnants of a fleet of beautiful old sailing day boats called Essex One Designs. Thankfully these boats along with all the other smaller craft had been removed for the winter and only a few sturdy working fishing boats remained. After the gale George hurried down to the harbour to check upon the fishing boats. He'd many friends in the fishing community and wanted to be on hand to offer help where he could. It had been a terrible storm and as he drove down Fort Hill past the police station and towards the harbour he looked out to sea, did a double take and gasped in surprise. The familiar lifeboat house situated about half way down the jetty was stranded, marooned out at sea; the jetty had collapsed and the timbers washed away. The gale and subsequent fall out became the talk of the town. Eventually a Wessex helicopter from nearby RAF Manston dropped members of the lifeboat crew out to the marooned boathouse. They were able to check over the lifeboat and the launching ramp. Eventually they managed to launch the boat and get her over to the safety of the neighbouring harbour at Ramsgate. Thankfully George's friends in the fishing community had weathered the storm and reported little damage to their vessels. Many local people came down to the seafront and beach to observe the damage and some began hauling large pieces of the jetty's structure away as souvenirs.

George was in the process of building a beautiful new home on the cliffs at Palm Bay and suddenly he hit upon the idea of salvaging a piece of the jetty for posterity and to grace his new home. It was only a few days before the destructive storm that he'd met with his architect and they had discussed the idea of a large stone and flint fireplace and a natural wood mantelpiece. George smiled and muttered to himself, "A piece of the historic jetty will make a wonderful mantle and provide an interesting talking point for my dinner guests." He solicited the help of his fisherman friends. A member of Margate Yacht Club even offered to loan their Ford Transit Van. Before long George had a fine piece of Ironwood stowed away in his garage waiting for completion of his house and its eventual installation over his newly constructed stone and flint fireplace.

By the time Christmas 1978 came around his new home was complete. The dried out wooden mantle over the new fireplace looked far better than George anticipated. Many friends stopped by to admire his new home and its main floor talking point. The newly constructed fireplace faced a large picture window overlooking the sea. On a clear day the Goodwin Sands were visible. However, despite everything looking so good George had a niggling feeling that something seemed to be missing. He felt that he needed something special to grace his mantelpiece. At fifty years old he remained a bachelor; his new home lacked a woman's touch. His walls were covered with bold, bright, eclectic pieces of art collected over his many years of business travel. He also owned several pieces of quirky, modern Danish furniture. "George, darling, you need something special to adorn your new mantelpiece," gushed Gloria one evening in early 1979 when several friends sat down to dinner at his new home. The next day George decided that he should definitely search for that something special.

It wasn't long before he found exactly what he was looking for, a couple of old black and white photographs of his deceased grandmother, Henrietta. His own mother, Ella, had passed away in 1977 and George inherited an old leather trunk hidden away in her attic filled with trinkets from the Victorian and Edwardian eras. There were some silver framed photographs and a beautiful lace wedding dress carefully wrapped in faded tissue paper. His mother's words came to mind, "George, when I'm dead and gone take good care of that old trunk up in my attic. Sell the house and the rest of my possessions but keep that trunk. It's really all that is left of your dear grandmother." As George rifled through the trunk, he recalled fond memories of childhood holiday visits to America and Grandma Henrietta. He shed a tear when he remembered that he was just twenty years old and away from home attending university when he received the news of her sudden, unexpected death of pneumonia and heart failure.

Henrietta was born in England in 1870 but grew up in the West Indies; her parents served in the diplomatic service and she was their much-loved only child. In 1898 her mother brought her to Europe to tour Italy and Switzerland and to visit relatives in Southern England. Sadly, at the grand old age of 28 Henrietta was considered to be on the shelf. Her parents were eager to see their only child married but unfortunately no suitable young men had crossed her path. George discovered an old diary in the trunk with entries written by Henrietta during the summer of 1898. They recounted a story of whirlwind romance and forbidden love in Margate. Henrietta and her mother were residing for the late summer and early autumn months at the very well-appointed and fashionable Hotel Metropole situated on the seafront at the end of the Margate jetty. They'd finished up a hectic late spring, early summer tour of Switzerland, Venice and the Italian Lakes and now it was time for mother and daughter to take in the sea air at Margate and connect with some relatives.

The original Margate jetty, also known as the pier, was initially constructed of wood in 1824. However, It needed constant repair so in later years Eugenius Birch designed and had it rebuilt of iron.

Construction begun in 1853 and when the new jetty was opened in 1855 it became the first iron seaside pier in the world. It was completed in 1857 and a pavilion was constructed a year later. This was used as a station building for steamship arrivals and departures. Unfortunately, on January 1st 1877 the jetty was sliced through by a storm driven wreck marooning some 40-50 people who weren't rescued until the next day! Another disaster occurred later that same year when on the 24th November a drifting vessel caused four thousand pounds worth of damage as the jetty was struck yet again! Additions were made in 1893 and again in 1900. In 1898 a building and a slipway was constructed to allow the Royal National Lifeboat Institution's Margate Lifeboat Station to be relocated to the jetty. The wood used was called Greenheart or Ironwood. Work on this new extension just happened to be taking place while Henrietta and her mother were resident at The Hotel Metropole.

Henrietta was bored with all the travelling and felt stifled by her demanding, critical and ever eagle-eyed mother. She felt under tremendous pressure to meet a suitable man and wed. Her parents had set the agenda, her life was mapped out and sadly there was no room for the real Henrietta. Her own hopes and dreams were constantly squashed or ignored and she always seemed to be dancing to someone else's tune. Despite the sunny weather and the fresh, exhilarating air of their recent visit to the Swiss Alps and the Italian Lakes Henrietta remained thin, sensitive, pale and frail. To the glamorous ladies who frequented the grand, airy public rooms at The Hotel Metropole she always appeared sickly. This was not surprising because deep down Henrietta felt that her very lifeblood was being sucked away. Mother suffocated her and in truth she knew that she'd become a mere ghost of her former self and that her life on earth had become untenable.

Mother and daughter had been in residence for three weeks when Henrietta began to take an interest in the work that seemed to be underway at the jetty. More to the point a young man had caught her eye! Edward was a local lad who'd recently finished up his apprenticeship as a carpenter and was now gainfully employed along with a number of other tradesmen to work upon the jetty extension. There was something about his relaxed, happy, tanned face that drew her in. His robust physique, pale blue eyes and shock of fair hair gave him the look of a Viking from days of old. Every day when mother and daughter strolled past the construction area the young man would tip his cap and Henrietta's heart would flutter. A week or so after these comings and goings Henrietta's mother went down with a mysterious, debilitating fever. A local doctor was called and confined her to bed rest for several weeks.

For the first time in months Henrietta was free to spend her days alone and she began to savour every single moment. As she strode out for her daily walks she would stop by and engage in brief conversations with her Viking beau. She wrote about him in her diary and he appeared in her dreams at night. She conjured up fairy tale stories in her mind of a blissful future together. Her skin began to glow as blood coursed through her veins; she gradually lost her pale, sickly appearance and there was a happy spring in her step as she took in the clean, fresh, Margate air.

One day Edward asked her to meet him late one evening and step out with him for a stroll along the beach. Mother was still confined to bed rest so it was easy for Henrietta to bid her goodnight and creep out of their suite of rooms and scurry down the fire escape steps unnoticed. This moonlit rendezvous became a regular fixture as August rolled into September. The couple would walk hand in hand along the sands, giggle, take off their shoes and paddle in the cool grey waters of the North Sea. They engaged in animated conversation and gradually fell in love. Henrietta shared stories from her difficult and lonely life in the West Indies and how she enjoyed a closeted, privileged, wealthy lifestyle. Her parents expected her to attend all of their fashionable parties, balls and social events. The pressure was always on to secure a suitable husband. She confided, "I feel so powerless. My mother and father rule with a rod of iron and sometimes I can't even breathe." Edward would throw back his head and laugh exclaiming, "Henrietta, we are chalk and cheese!"

He too shared stories but they were of his humble origins and his difficult upbringing in Margate. In comparison Edward's life was quite ordinary and particularly hard. Unlike Henrietta's it lacked glamour and colour. His parents had little money. His father was a fisherman. He had many siblings and he remembered all the times in the past when there wasn't enough food to feed them all. "I've always worked hard; my parents are loving and supportive but we all have to pitch in to simply keep the family afloat. We're honest folk, always ready and willing to help a neighbour who may have fallen upon hard times but there's nothing special about us."

Nevertheless, despite the obvious deep social chasm between them, Henrietta had fallen head over heels in love. She was enchanted and intrigued by Edward's simple, humble life and by his honesty. There was no reason to make small talk. She felt safe in his strong arms and for the first time in her life she began to feel like a real person and not someone else's puppet. The ever-watchful ladies frequenting the public rooms at The Metropole Hotel passed away their time in idle gossip. They were the first to observe Henrietta's transformation. She was blossoming into a happy beautiful woman. They nodded knowingly to each other and in hushed voices they speculated as to what exactly Henrietta might be up to as her poor mother remained upstairs and bed ridden.

The lovers were six weeks into the thrill of their fairy-tale courtship when they made a secret tryst. Using all of his savings Edward gave Henrietta a small silver band purchased from S.H. Cutting Jewellers and Goldsmiths in Margate Old Town Marketplace. It was engraved with their names and a little heart. However, he knew all along in his own heart of hearts that Henrietta's parents would never accept his proposal for her hand in marriage. He knew only too well that they came from two different worlds that were never meant to meet. Nevertheless, the silver band was a token of his friendship and love. The unfortunate reality simply being he came from the wrong side of the tracks; he lacked pedigree, education, finesse and money. Henrietta knew it too but the two lovers were spellbound and caught up in some kind of a magical web that left them oblivious to the real world and to common sense. Henrietta even visited a local dressmaker and was fitted for a lovely white lace wedding gown. She smuggled Edward into her hotel bedroom late at night and they spent several nights together as man and wife.

Sadly, the fairy-tale romance all came to a most distressing and very abrupt end as September turned to October. Nights were drawing in; the weather suddenly became much colder and the wealthy tourists began to pack their trunks and make the necessary arrangements to return home. The season was coming to a close. Henrietta's mother began to feel much better and one sunny day she ventured downstairs to spend some time in the elegant public rooms of the fashionable Hotel Metropole. Mrs. Byrd waddled over and befriended her. She was the first lady to tell tales of Henrietta's comings and goings. "If I were you, I would scoop your daughter up and head back to the West Indies as soon as possible. My dear, surprise is most important in these delicate matters. Secretly make your travel arrangements and whisk her away before she has time to make or get into trouble. Mark my word dear, she has some kind of plan and us ladies feel that she's up to no good."

An angry woman with fire in her heart can move mountains. Within two days a return passage to the West Indies had been secured for mother and daughter. They were to board a steam ship bound for London, one of the regular boats that docked alongside the Margate jetty. A transfer booking to a larger ship that plied the Atlantic to New York then a transfer to another smaller vessel heading for the Caribbean Island of Barbados would follow. By the end of November mother and daughter would be home and just in time for the hectic social calendar of Christmas celebrations.

Henrietta was heartbroken and taken completely by surprise. Returning on October 14th from her early morning stroll she discovered two of the hotel maids in her room busily at work packing her trunks. When questioned Ethel simply replied, "Miss Henrietta your mother instructed us to quickly prepare your luggage as you'll both be leaving for London on the 2pm steamship sailing from the jetty." It took almost an hour for Henrietta to come to her senses after the sudden shock of learning about her mother's machinations. There was no time to meet with Edward or to bid him farewell. No last opportunity to feel his embrace and rest safely in his strong arms. It was the moment that she'd always dreaded but the two lovers both always knew in their hearts that such a time would surely come around. Henrietta sat at her writing desk by the window overlooking the jetty; in the distance she could see the men working away on the extension. Her world had suddenly become cold, grey and lifeless. Her hopes and dreams were shattered. She wrote a few simple sentences since she knew Edward had limited reading skills. She explained her swift departure and declared once again her enduring love for him. She promised that one day she would return to Margate and find him. She asked him to wait for her. Summoning one of the hotel bellboys she asked that he discreetly venture onto the jetty, find the works foreman who could pass her letter onto Edward. From her purse she pulled out a shilling to ensure that her letter would arrive safely into Edward's hands.

The return sea voyage to the Caribbean was long and tedious and towards the end Henrietta began to feel very sick in the mornings. She attributed this to the rough weather encountered by their steamship but once home the morning sickness continued and eventually, she consulted with her doctor. Her pregnancy diagnosis was a total shock and a major dilemma. The truth was that she remained unmarried and this was an unacceptable predicament for a young woman from her social standing. She dreaded having to face her parents; she feared that she might be cast out and sent to some far-off place to deal with her shame, perhaps to her distant Aunt Clara in America. These things happened but were definitely frowned upon in her own social circle especially when the father of her child was a lowly illiterate carpenter!

The long voyage home took its toll on her mother too; the mysterious sickness troubling her in Margate seemed to return. She took to her bed again; the doctor was called and as the weeks went by, she became extremely frail. Henrietta's father, in his constant worry for his wife's welfare, suddenly became sick too. This time the doctor was able to give a firm diagnosis. It was the dreaded Dengue Fever, the scourge of the tropics. Tragically, both parents passed away together on New Year's Eve 1898. Henrietta had kept her pregnancy secret and at barely three months along no one suspected that she was a young woman facing an awful predicament. Being an only child Henrietta would inherit her parent's fortune. She wrote to her Aunt Clara in America and asked if she could visit whilst she planned what to do with the rest of her life. She was eager to leave Barbados; she certainly didn't want to face her parent's friends and their diplomatic colleagues with the embarrassment and shame that she would surely bring to their good family name, their reputation, respected social standing and to their memory.

Aunt Clara, her father's younger sister, had married Henry a successful American industrial businessman of German descent and they lived in a fashionable suburb of Reading, Pennsylvania called Wyomissing. Tragically, in the early evening of September 19th, 1890 Henry had the misfortune to be involved in a three-train collision. It all happened in the vicinity of Shoemakersville, near Reading. 22 dead bodies were removed from the wreckage site. Henry was a passenger on The Pottsville Express as it hit coal train cars on the track. The coal train had collided earlier with a freight train and coal cars had been thrown onto the opposite track and into the path of the Pottsville Express. Henry was badly injured and passed away shortly afterwards. Although the accident had occurred over eight years ago Clara still grieved his loss. She was lonely and welcomed Henrietta's request. Certainly, it would be both interesting and exciting to have her niece to stay for a while. The couple had never been blessed with children of their own and although Clara had many friends there was always a huge void. She looked forward to helping her young niece navigate her own grief and helping her to decide what to do next. At 28 years old Henrietta was unmarried and already Clara was thinking about eligible young men amongst her own circle of elite friends. Reading, Pennsylvania was full of rich, successful, conservatively minded industrialists who lived in large mansions. Some of them had lost their wives in childbirth and Clara had already drawn up a small list of potential suitors.

Of course, when Henrietta arrived after yet another long steamship voyage to Philadelphia and a train journey from the city to Reading, Pennsylvania she was tired, apprehensive and four months along. However, her great secret was still intact and at first glance it was not obvious that she was carrying a child. It was cold; snow lay on the ground and the wealthy town with its grand mansions was a far cry from the warm, tropical shores of colonial Barbados. Henrietta immediately noticed that there were no black faces. There were many churches, it was mainly a Protestant town and blessed with little crime. Aunt Clara welcomed her with open arms. She lived in a large, elegant, comfortable mansion called Easton. Clara had a housekeeper, cook, kitchen maid, lady's maid, butler and several gardeners and handymen on staff. Her deceased husband had left her well provided for in his will. Clara inherited his business dealings and she'd astutely appointed two good managers to continue his successful work. Money was the least of Clara's worries.

That first night whilst alone in her spacious guest bedroom Henrietta sobbed. Aunt Clara was a woman of considerable social standing. She was a regular member of her local church congregation. She had many influential friends. She volunteered in the community and was highly respected. She was a woman with high morals just like her brother and his wife. Henrietta agonized and chided herself over her decision to show up on her aunt's doorstep and avail herself of Clara's gracious hospitality. In her frustration and grief, she questioned and scolded herself. "How can I have been so stupid? Coming here is probably a major mistake. Aunt Clara won't understand and I'll be bringing shame upon her household too. I was so stupid to get myself into this predicament in the first place. Passion, impulse, and the heat of the moment selfishly guided me. How could I have been this naïve and stupid? I certainly wasn't guided by common sense, reason and practicality. Yet I loved Edward and I'm carrying his child. I just don't know what to do, I need help but there's nobody that I completely trust to turn to."

Help duly arrived that very night in her restless sleep. It came in her dreams and in the shape of a wizened, roly-poly woman. She looked like a gypsy. The old woman stood at the end of the familiar Margate jetty near the steamship pavilion. It was icy cold; she shuddered and wrapped her shawl tightly around her shoulders. The wind blew and whistled wildly; the sea was rough and large grey waves capped with white foam crashed noisily around the pilings supporting the jetty. Henrietta suddenly remembered that she'd seen this old woman working in the dressmaker's shop in Old Town Margate. This was the very shop where she'd purchased her beautiful white lace wedding gown. The old woman pointed to the large clock mounted high up on the steamship pavilion wall then she turned and spoke with both clarity and authority over the noisy wind and the crashing of the waves.

"Heed the time, Henrietta. In five months, your child will be born. Remember that your child has a father, the man you loved. The child's father has a right to know his own flesh and blood. When the time is right you must return to Margate and make such a meeting possible. My dear, in another time, another age, marriage to Edward might have been possible but right now you must realize that you come from two worlds that are separate. Neither of you will find the happiness that you once had as carefree lovers walking on the sands. Henrietta that time has passed. You both stepped into a third world, the fairy-tale world. You must find the courage to face up to reality and move on. Be strong, face up to your responsibilities as a young mother, stop hiding your child and face the world. You cannot live out a lie any longer. You were right to leave Barbados behind and protect your parent's good name. Your Aunt Clara is a sensible woman she'll help you to navigate the stormy waters of the next few years. You can trust her. She'll protect you. Mother and child will find a safe harbour at Easton. One day you'll find love again and you will marry but for now Henrietta do the right thing and divulge your secret."

The old woman faded away and Henrietta woke with a start. She lay in bed reflecting and knew in her heart that she needed to sit down with Aunt Clara and lay all of her cards upon the table. Opportunity presented itself the next day as the two ladies sat in Easton's elegant drawing room sipping tea from her fine blue willow china edged with gold. Henrietta was nervous. It was cold outside, snowflakes were falling and the spacious grounds, visible from the large drawing room windows, were covered in a sparkling white blanket. The snow suddenly reminded Aunt Clara of her own strange dream. She sat upright and ready because in her heart she knew exactly what Henrietta was about to confide.

Actually, from the moment that the two women met and embraced on the snow-covered steps of Easton Clara had sensed deep within her inner knowing that all was not well and that there was much more to Henrietta than first met the eye. She too had experienced a strange dream several weeks before Henrietta's arrival. In truth Clara had been lonely, sad and bored for many years. Easton seemed like a house without a soul. It was beautiful but cavernous and in more recent years it felt empty and lifeless. In the early days when she and Henry had moved in as a wealthy young couple, they decided to call it Easton because it was an old English name meaning *magical.* They both yearned for a magical place to raise their children but tragically that time never came and now Henry was gone, lost forever. Clara cried for many years following his untimely death and pleaded with God for help on so many occasions. Eventually it came in the shape of a wizened, roly-poly old woman resembling a gypsy. The old woman appeared in a dream not long after Christmas 1898. The world was white, covered in a blanket of crisp snow sparkling in the sunlight. She stood under the old oak tree in the grounds of Easton shuddering in the cold icy air and pulling her shawl closely around her chest. She had kind, piercing eyes but they seemed to see right into Clara's broken heart. Then she spoke with clarity and authority and her words rang in Clara's ears for many days following her visit.

"Clara, the loneliness of Easton will soon change for you. A child is coming who'll break the spell and bring about transformation. Easton will become the beautiful, magical place that you and Henry always wanted. Your home will ring with laughter and joy and you'll find the peace that you've yearned for and sought out for so long. This child will help you to heal all of your broken pieces. A young woman is with child and she desperately needs your help. Do not cast her out, be strong and rise above your prejudices and of those around you, heads will turn but welcome her into your home. Mark my word that only good will come from your generosity and from extending a hand of tolerance and friendship."

Then the strange old woman was gone, faded away into the snowy landscape and Clara woke up with a start. It wasn't long after this memorable dream, carefully recorded in her journal, that she received a telegram from Barbados. Her brother and his wife had passed away and Henrietta, their only child, was asking if she could visit and stay awhile.

Sitting comfortably in the spacious drawing room sipping their tea the two women engaged in casual conversation mainly concerning Wyomissing and Aunt Clara's well-connected friends. Eventually Henrietta, tired of dancing around, bit the bullet and suddenly blurted out her secret.

"Aunt Clara, I'm having a child. The truth is that I left Barbados keeping this secret close to my heart. I didn't want to soil my parent's memory particularly their good name or their fine reputation. My father worked hard in the diplomatic service, they were influential and accomplished many good things for the island and its people. Now that they've passed away my only wish is that their friends and colleagues look upon their memory with fondness and that they do not become the focus of scandalous gossip."

Clara sighed and reached over to take Henrietta's delicate hand. "That's very noble my dear and I'll help you. However, when people see that you are with child, they will surely ask questions, there will be gossip and my good name and reputation may also be in jeopardy. Firstly, you'd better tell me your story and exactly who is your child's father?"

For the remainder of that snowy February afternoon the two women engaged in deep conversation. Henrietta talked about her time in Europe with her mother and how they eventually came to England and spent the late summer and early autumn in Margate. She recounted how she caught Edward's eye on the Margate jetty, their budding courtship strolling hand in hand along the Margate sands, the silver band Edward purchased from S.H. Cutting and her beautiful yet unworn white lace wedding dress. She discussed her mother's mysterious illness, her own sense of personal freedom and her traumatically swift return to Barbados. With a broken heart Henrietta related how she'd written immediately to Edward care of the Margate jetty works manager and the Hotel Metropole. She told him about her pregnancy, her parent's sudden death and how she planned to leave Barbados and visit her Aunt Clara in Pennsylvania. She even included in that letter Clara's address in Wyomissing but sadly there had been no communication from Edward.

Aunt Clara sat back and silently reflected for some time and then drawing in a deep breath she said, "Henrietta let's be sensible and practical. Wear the silver ring because you were as good as married and Edward is missing. It will make things a lot easier while you remain here at Easton. Look upon my beautiful home as your home too. Raise your child here or at least until your circumstances change. Henry's mother gave me a pretty heart shaped ruby ring surrounded by diamonds shortly before she died. It has been hidden away in a little box for years because Henry gave me so many rings and I never got around to wearing it. I'm going to give you that ring. Wear it together with your silver band and people won't ask quite so many questions. When they enquire about your child's father simply tell them that he is missing." Clara suddenly drew back her head and chuckled, "I've just realized that you'll be residing here in Wyomissing, a town with missing in its name! Henrietta, I suggest that you write to your dear

Edward two more times but if after your three letters you receive no communication then please let him go. Please move on with your life, enjoy your child. We can raise the child together. Are you open to this possibility?"

Henrietta stood up and embraced her Aunt Clara fondly. For the first time in her life, she felt that she had a good advocate. Here was someone who wanted to help and wasn't there to judge her. Here was someone who extended a hand of friendship and understanding. The heart shaped ruby and diamond ring was magnificent and wearing it with Edward's simple silver band helped to put a stop to household and local gossip.

Aunt Clara brought Henrietta to consult with her homoeopathic doctor who gave her a few doses of the remedy *Ignatia*. This helped her to process her acute grief, the loss of her parents and of her dear Edward because despite sending two more letters she'd received no communication at all from her lover. The remedy helped to put a stop to all the nights where she'd lain in bed sobbing and it helped her adjust to her new life living with Aunt Clara in Wyomissing.

Ella was born in Reading, Pennsylvania at the Homoeopathic Hospital in mid-July 1899. When mother and baby arrived home Easton was looking at its best. The gardens were full of the scent of fragrant, colourful roses. Aunt Clara's wealthy friends brought beautiful baby gifts and a nanny was engaged to help out in the nursery. Clara's handymen transformed two of the bedrooms into a suite for the new baby and Easton began to ring with joy and laughter just as the old gypsy woman in Clara's dream had foretold.

Aunt Clara had always been a keen supporter of homoeopathic medicine. A German physician called Alolph Lippe, who later became very famous in homoeopathic circles, had brought homoeopathy to Reading Pennsylvania in 1840. Dr. John Henry Behne from Bavaria continued in Dr. Lippe's footsteps and developed a large practice in Reading until his death in 1876. There were several other practitioners in these early days so by the later 19th century homoeopathy was well established in the area. In 1882, the Hahnemann Medical Society of Reading was organized in the South Fourth Street office of Dr. Samuel Rittenhouse who would later play an important role in the formation of the Homoeopathic Hospital in Reading. In 1888 Dr. Erastus Scholl headed a group of homoeopathic physicians who organized the Homoeopathic Dispensary Association. The group operated a small dispensary at the corner of Plum and Franklin Streets providing much needed care to the poor of the city. In November of 1888 seventeen women established the first Women's Auxiliary of the Homoeopathic Hospital Association providing maintenance funds for the Dispensary through membership dues, collection of donations, and parlour entertainments. Its objective was also to raise awareness in Reading of the need for a homoeopathic hospital. When the hospital eventually opened it was totally furnished by the Auxiliary. By December 31st, 1891 the Auxiliary had grown to 250 members. Following Henry's untimely death in 1890 friends introduced Clara to the Auxiliary and since that initial introduction she'd spent much of her time supporting their efforts. On July 1, 1891 the hospital opened its doors to the City of Reading.

Ella was almost twelve years old when Henrietta received yet another surprise visit from the old gypsy woman of her dreams. Life was comfortable and settled for both mother and daughter in Wyomissing. Henrietta had inherited her parent's fortune. Clara was kind and generous; Easton had become their home. Over Ella's early childhood years Clara introduced Henrietta to the Women's Homoeopathic Auxiliary and both women enthusiastically threw themselves into charity work. Of course, questions were asked in those early years of Ella's life. A few heads would turn and there had been many knowing nods and glances. However, in more recent years, mother and daughter had become totally integrated into Wyomissing society and were accepted.

Henrietta's memories of Margate and Edward were not completely forgotten. Henrietta had a few suitors as Ella grew older but she tended to keep them at arm's length. Sometimes she would lie in bed and wonder if Edward was still in Margate. She had so many unanswered questions and as time went on, she began to feel that she needed some kind of closure. She began to feel that it was time to finally move on.

The old gypsy woman appeared in a dream just after midnight on February 14th 1911, Valentine's Day. Once again, she was standing on the icy cold wind-swept Margate jetty pointing to the large clock on the steamship pavilion. She spoke with authority and urgency.

> *"Henrietta, heed the time. It's time that you took Ella on a voyage to England. It's time that she has the opportunity to meet her father. Spend the next few months planning and ensure that she's in Margate to celebrate her 12th birthday."*

Her message was urgent, short and to the point and then she vanished.

Valentine's Day was always a painful reminder of the past. In the early years Henrietta would climb the spiral staircase up into the attic and open an old leather chest stored away in the vast roof space. She carefully opened the faded tissue paper and pulled out the beautiful lace wedding dress and fingered it gently. The dress brought back fond memories of Margate and the short but thrilling times that she'd enjoyed with Edward by her side. In more recent years, with the passage of time, that chest gathered dust and cobwebs as it lay quite forgotten amongst old unwanted furniture, lamps and bric-a-brac.

Henrietta woke up from her dream with a start; she suddenly remembered the old gypsy woman's words when she'd first arrived at Easton as a pregnant, fearful young woman hesitant to share her secret. She realized that it was indeed time to take her precious Ella to Margate and to search for her daughter's father. Arrangements were made to take a steamship from New York to London arriving on July 1st. Mother and daughter arranged to stay in London for a few days to take in all the city sights and then travel onto Margate by train. Henrietta made reservations to stay for several weeks at the Hotel Metropole at the end of the Margate jetty.

Curiously Ella had never broached the subject of her father. She was a sweet, intelligent girl blossoming into a delightful young lady. Ella had a kind nature, popular amongst her friends and always keen to help her mother and Aunt Clara with the Ladies Auxiliary Homoeopathic Charity Work. Henrietta took the opportunity during the lengthy steamship voyage across the Atlantic to sit down with her young daughter and to talk honestly and frankly about the circumstances surrounding her birth. Much to Henrietta's relief Ella seemed to take the news in her stride. It was as if she knew that her mother and Aunt Clara had some secret that they were keeping from her. Being an intelligent young lady and much older than her years she'd put two and two together and speculated that one day, in her own time, her mother would tell her about her father.

Margate hadn't changed much from the late summer of 1898 when Henrietta and Edward, as young lovers, had strolled along the sands. The donkeys were out and about and there were deckchairs on the crowded beach. The jetty and the Hotel Metropole were bustling with activity since Margate was in the height of the busy tourist season. Henrietta immediately began to make enquiries around the town and it wasn't long before she traced Edward to a small cottage located near to St John's church and the donkey stables. Ella agreed that Henrietta should make the first contact and determine if he was even amenable to meeting his daughter.

Well, Thursday July 6th 1911 turned out to was an extremely difficult day for Henrietta. Edward lived in a very small, humble dwelling. Two small grubby looking children played outside in the street near to the front door. When she knocked a young woman answered. She was pretty but looked extremely weary and was heavily pregnant. She eyed her well-dressed and carefully groomed visitor suspiciously. Henrietta introduced herself as an old friend who was visiting Margate and who just wanted to stop by and greet Edward. It was obvious that this young woman was his wife and as she nervously twisted the small silver band on her wedding finger, she told Henrietta to return at 7 o'clock that evening. "Edward is working at his carpenter's shop up on Sparrow Castle, he's very busy during the day." Henrietta smiled and graciously thanking her she turned and immediately decided that she couldn't possibly return to his home again. As she walked down the road, she asked an old man if he knew the location of Sparrow Castle. Thankfully the curiously named old alleyway was nearby. He assured Henrietta that she could walk there quite easily. Henrietta gathered courage, found the carpenter's shop on Sparrow Castle and gingerly entered into the dusty working space. Several men were busily occupied. Heads turned as she made her entrance and immediately Edward recognized her. He quickly put down his tools and rushed over to shepherd her out of the door and away from the prying eyes of the other workmen.

It was an awkward reunion. Edward was particularly embarrassed because he'd never returned Henrietta's letters. He'd decided to let her go shortly after her swift departure from Margate back in October 1898 because in his heart he'd always realized that their passionate relationship was doomed. When news of her pregnancy arrived, he sought advice from his close-knit family and they all told him in no uncertain terms that she was a woman of financial means and that it was best for everyone concerned to keep quiet and to forget. However, over the years he'd often wondered about his child and pondered over Henrietta's welfare. Edward also yearned for some kind of closure. Brushing everything that had happened between them under the carpet and pretending that nothing had happened, especially when a child was involved, just didn't sit right in his soul. He seemed particularly alarmed when Henrietta disclosed that she'd just visited his home and had talked briefly with his young wife.

"Edward, I want nothing from you. I've made my life these past 12 years in Pennsylvania. Ella and I live with my Aunt Clara. Life is comfortable and meaningful but I do want closure and a chance to move on. I want to close this chapter of my life. Of course, I now see that you're married and have your own young family and another child is on the way. I haven't come to make trouble but I do think that your beautiful daughter, Ella, should be given the opportunity to meet and know something of her father."

Thankfully Edward agreed as long as his wife remained in the dark. Together they hatched a plan to meet on Wednesday July 12th, Ella's birthday at 4pm for afternoon tea at The Lyons Corner House Café on Margate High Street. Edward also insisted that his mother, Florence, accompany him. Curiously July 12th was also his mother's 60th birthday and this would give him a good reason to excuse himself early in the afternoon from work and wouldn't raise any suspicions at home either. The family had planned a party for his mother on Sunday July 16th but Edward felt suspicions wouldn't be raised by this extra event on her actual birthday; after all he was her oldest son. Henrietta insisted on paying for the fancy afternoon tea and said that she would make all the necessary arrangements. "Edward, I just need you and Florence to turn up and spend a few hours enjoying meeting your delightful daughter. Then we'll walk out of your life unless you choose to continue to engage with Ella. Just know that we'll be discreet and certainly don't want to cause any trouble for you at home."

It was a memorable afternoon spent sipping tea and eating dainty cucumber and salmon sandwiches, cakes and scones. Ella delighted her father and grandmother. Florence could see how much she resembled Edward; she had the same blonde hair, piercing pale blue eyes and Viking looks, even similar mannerisms. Ella talked about her life in Wyomissing living at Easton with her mother and dear Aunt Clara. She mentioned her friends and her pet spaniel. She shared her interests particularly her love of drawing, painting and art history and of her hope that one day she could study at art school and pursue a career as an artist. Edward talked about his small carpentry business. He described what life was like living in Margate and reluctantly he briefly mentioned his wife, Norah, and their two young children. When they bid their farewells Edward and his mother agreed to keep in touch with Ella. They would exchange letters twice a year at Christmas and on her birthday. Henrietta sighed with relief once they were back at The Hotel Metropole.

Feeling that the afternoon went well and that her daughter had finally met her father she felt that she now had the peace and the closure that she'd eagerly sought out for so long. On the spur of the moment Henrietta suddenly said to Ella, "Let's check out of the hotel tomorrow, our business in Margate is complete and there's no pressing reason for us to remain here. We can take a boat to France then onwards to Paris and visit some of the art galleries!" Ella beamed with delight. She felt her mother's happiness and relief and agreed that their time in Margate had come to a successful end and that it was time to move on and to explore the world.

Henrietta and Ella really enjoyed the rest of that 1911 summer in Europe. As time passed letters were duly exchanged at Christmas time and upon Ella's birthday. However, in 1915, when she was 16 years old, an unexpected letter arrived at Easton in early November announcing Edward's untimely death. Florence felt compelled to write the lengthy letter addressed to both Henrietta and Ella. When war broke out in the summer of 1914 Edward had volunteered along with many of the brave young men from Margate. This letter described how he'd tragically fallen in Flanders Fields. His family were distraught especially Norah and her three young children. Florence had absolutely no idea how her oldest son's family would survive without the help of their breadwinner. She was heading into old age with limited financial resources and certainly there wasn't enough to support Edward's young family. Henrietta, Clara and Ella were upset and dismayed when they read Florence's letter. They sat down and talked for some time about how to respond appropriately. They knew that Norah knew nothing of young Ella and they knew that Edward had always wanted to keep it that way. "We must honour his wishes but we do have an obligation to help the family as best we can albeit from a distance," declared Aunt Clara.

Clara took it upon herself to make the necessary arrangements. She was a wealthy woman and certainly had the means to set funds aside to help the struggling young family. She consulted with her bankers who made arrangements with a Margate bank to hold money in trust for Edward's family. An account was established in Ella's name at Lloyd's Bank in King Street, Margate but the benefactor's information was to be kept private. It wasn't long before a considerable sum was deposited. There was enough money to cover all living expenses and education for many years and it was to be made available on a monthly basis until Edward's youngest child reached the age of 21. At that time the remaining funds would be released to Norah that's if she still remained unmarried otherwise what was left would be Ella's to use as she wished. Clara shared all the details by letter with Florence who was overcome with relief but extremely anxious as to how she could possibly explain away such an arrangement without arousing Norah's suspicion.

The answer came to Florence in a dream. A stout old lady appeared at the end of Margate's jetty. It was icy cold; the wind was whipping up the grey sea and it had begun to snow. The old lady pulled her shawl tightly around her chest. She had a kindly face and was pointing to the large clock on the steamship pavilion. The strange woman seemed familiar and Florence suddenly remembered seeing her working away at a sewing machine upon a number of occasions in one of the haberdashers and drapers stores in Margate Old Town. Then the old woman began to speak with clarity and authority above the whistling wind and the falling snow.

"Florence, time is marching on. Edward's family urgently needs help so you must set aside your worries and only think of the greater good. All things work together for the greater good. Money will be available soon at Lloyd's Bank for the young family. A generous woman, an aunt from America, has provided and that's all that Norah needs to know. She's a sensible lady, she has prayed for help since Edward passed and now those prayers are answered. There's no need for questions and there's no need for answers. Tell Norah to visit the bank on the first Monday of every month until her

youngest child turns 21 and there'll always be money available to provide for the family until that time."

Before Florence could speak the old woman had faded into the snowy seascape. She woke with a start and the next day she hurried down to Margate Old Town to try and find her but when she enquired at all the haberdashers and drapers shops no one had ever seen or heard of such a woman.

Since that very special 12th birthday visit to England with her mother Ella had been drawn to her parent's country of birth. Of course, Henrietta had lived there in her early years before her parents were called abroad to serve as diplomats to Barbados. Opportunity to explore Britain opened up for Ella in the fall of 1919, following the First World War. She applied and gained a place to study at Bedford College, established in 1849 and becoming part of the University of London in 1900. It was amongst the first places in Britain where women could access higher education.

At the weekends Ella often took the train to Margate and visited Florence for Sunday afternoon tea. The young woman was able to keep a beneficent watch, albeit at a distance, upon Norah's welfare and that of her stepbrothers and sister. At the age of 24 and in her final year at university she met her husband a very successful London businessman. Eventually they made their life in England living in an idyllic village beside the river Thames where Ella established an art studio and gallery.

Their only son, George, was born in 1928 and Ella took him every summer back to America to visit her mother. Henrietta eventually inherited Easton when Aunt Clara passed away. In his younger years the family would also visit Margate and it was such fond memories of these seaside holidays that drew George to Margate as a young man in his thirties. He'd eventually decided to make his own home by the sea. "Margate is in my blood," he confessed to his mother one day and she nodded. Ella and Henrietta had both felt the town calling them. Of course, it was only natural because the family had such deep connections and history with the little seaside holiday town.

As for Norah, she happily married again when her children were older. Aunt Clara's money had been a blessing, the family never wanted, there was always food on the table, the rent was paid on time and there was enough money every month to ensure that her three children were well educated and able to pursue the careers of their choice. They all chose to remain close to home. Family was important. Sometimes, in her quiet moments, Norah would ponder over the money that she'd collected every month from Lloyd's Bank until her youngest turned 21. Then her busy mind always turned to that July day in 1911 when a well-groomed woman knocked on her door. However, Norah was wise. She learnt to put those worrying thoughts to one side, locked away in a dusty trunk somewhere. She learnt that sometimes in life it was best not to ask questions and not to seek answers. It was best not to know and just to be grateful that somewhere she had a guardian angel watching out for her.

Henrietta met the love of her life when she was 55. He was a retired homoeopathic doctor who lived locally. They eventually married spending many wonderful years of their life together living at her beloved Easton in Wyomissing. By the time of her marriage the beautiful white lace dress made for her in Margate was far too small. Upon the eve of her wedding, she climbed the stairs to the attic and opened the old leather trunk. She peeled away the faded tissue paper and held the dress in her arms. Her mind wandered to her fond memories of Edward, the father of her wonderful Ella, and how his life had been tragically cut short in Flanders Fields. Then her mind wandered to her parents who'd died so quickly upon her return to Barbados and to Aunt Clara's unfailing generosity and friendship. She thought about all the good that Clara's money had done for Norah and her young family. Henrietta finally thought about all her own good works with The Homoeopathic Auxiliary and how this involvement had brought her to yet another new chapter in her life. She sighed and carefully packed the beautiful dress away. It didn't feel right to sell or to donate it to one of the charity organizations. However, she knew in her heart that she would never open this particular trunk again. The future of its contents would rest in someone else's hands when she was dead and gone. It was time for her to move on, say goodbye and it finally felt right to do so. She had the closure that she'd sought for so long. It was finally time.

Poppy opened her eyes and lovingly fingered the piece of driftwood. Jack the lad stirred and she muttered to her faithful companion, "This piece of wood has a remarkable history. I wonder if it was part of the Margate jetty and if young Edward handled it back in 1898 when he was working on the Margate jetty extension?" Then Poppy suddenly remembered that an elderly lady called Gloria had stopped by the shop shortly after Christmas giving her a beautiful white lace wedding dress probably dating from the late 1800's. Gloria explained that it once belonged to her good friend George's grandmother. She also explained George's recent passing and how she'd helped to clear his home. Apparently, it was due for demolition to make way for a new road. Poppy's eye caught sight of the beautiful vintage white lace dresses hanging gracefully on the rack and then down at the dainty silk slippers lined up along the top of the Ironwood. She smiled to herself as she recalled the old wizened woman who had appeared at the end of the jetty in so many dreams and she knew in her heart that Madam Popoff had intervened yet again.

Poppy turned to Jack the Lad and said, "All things are connected. I do hope that one day a beautiful bride wears Henrietta's wedding dress. That dress has waited long enough!" She sighed, hurried to the back room to wash her cup and gathered up her coat, scarf and hat. She scooped Jack the Lad up and turned off the lights. As she crossed the threshold and started to lock the door with the ancient iron key, Poppy remembered the beginning of this special day. It had all begun with the blessing of the sea. She reflected upon the Archangel Michael, the great protector. Her mind turned to Madam Popoff and she once again wondered if she too were an angel.

The next day, shortly after opening up, old Cecil stopped by for a cup of coffee and a friendly chat. He immediately spotted the driftwood and exclaimed, "Poppy you have some Greenheart there! It's part of the old Margate jetty. Hold onto that wood as it's a remarkable piece of the town's history!" Poppy smiled, "Cecil, that piece of wood has history and yes, it definitely belongs here in Madam Popoff's Vintage Emporium." As the day went on Poppy wondered who had saved it from the demolition of George's home. However, she quickly checked herself knowing by now that sometimes it was not for her to ask questions and not for her to know the answers and that magical, unseen forces always seemed to be at work.

That night as Poppy lay in bed, she began to reflect upon the Margate jetty story and the entwined lives of Henrietta, Edward, Aunt Clara, Ella, Norah and her family. She mused over how much she'd learnt about the ups and downs of life since meeting and working with Madam Popoff. Her thoughts turned to the important place that forgiveness, flexibility, compassion, optimism and following one's dreams seemed to be key to keeping healthy in mind, body and spirit. Poppy reflected upon homeopathic remedies and how much *Ignatia* helped Henrietta to move on. Finally, her thoughts turned to Dr. Edward Bach and his flower essences. She felt sure that many of these essences would have helped, particularly *Bach Rescue Remedy*, so very helpful in times of acute distress and trauma. She thought about poor Henrietta and the sudden shock she must have experienced because the rug had been pulled from under her feet. Returning from an idyllic early morning stroll along the beach she'd witnessed her possessions being hastily packed up because her mother had secretly arranged their swift departure. There was no time to bid her darling Edward goodbye. Poppy shed a tear and as she floated away into the land of dreams, she thought how tested and difficult being human and living life on planet earth could be.

Wartime

Maria Popoff was unsettled. In fact, she'd been extremely unsettled for many months as she'd anxiously watched events unfolding in Europe. Ancient relatives lived at one time in the Ukraine but distant Cousin Sergei; the last of their very long line, passed away from Coronavirus back in August of 2021. Maria often focused upon Vladimir Putin's stony face, his beady eyes and pursed lips. She perceived the dense, dark energy cloud that surrounded him. Shuddering she knew deep in her heart that this man was in many ways a walking time bomb. In early February, as reports filtered into the news of Russian troops gathering on the borders of Ukraine, she began pacing anxiously up and down the corridors and stairs late at night when everyone else had left and she had the silent, cavernous St. Eustace to herself. She wrung her hands tightly together, as tears would flow down her tanned, wrinkled and anxious face.

Maria had known the ugly, evil face of war for so long. Experiencing at first hand its destruction, the many broken pieces that it left in its wake and the shattered lives of innocent bystanders caught up in the cross fire. She'd looked into the hearts of the brave, innocent young men and women sent to the slaughter and she was weary. She remembered being in the Crimea back on October 15th 1854 and recalled Alfred, Lord Tennyson's famous poem, The Charge of the Light Brigade.

> *"Half a league, half a league,*
> *Half a league onward.*
> *All in the valley of Death*
> *Rode the six hundred."*

Maria found herself in Flanders Fields during World War One driving a battered Red Cross ambulance and plucking the mortally wounded from the battlefields. She remembered all too well the agonizing screams of the dying and the sight of limbs torn from young bodies because they haunted her dreams for years afterwards. Walking the tunnels of Ramsgate during the Second World War she knew what it was like to be displaced, homeless and confined to a cold, dank subterranean existence. Now it was about to happen all over again and she wept enough tears to fill the retention pond at the rear of St. Eustace.

Putin commanded his troops to begin the onslaught on February 24th and today Wednesday, March 2nd the battle was in its seventh day. Maria watched with horror as the BBC news broadcast scenes of destruction from familiar places that she'd once visited in the distant past. She saw the lines of fearful, distressed residents fleeing for their lives and the stoicism and bravery of menfolk who were staying behind determined to fight for their country and its independence. Maria's heart was heavy as she wondered if planet Earth was on the verge of World War 3. At 6pm she closed the doors and gathered everyone around the large oak table in the sewing room. Today St. Eustace folk would decide how they could best help those in Ukraine.

Bella and Harriet invited Pastor Joe and Linda busied herself by making and bringing pots of tea and slices of chocolate cake to the large oak table. Following an hour of focused dialogue, they decided upon a spring festival. After all it was March and the weather this time of the year was particularly nice and warm with mainly clear blue skies and gentle winds. Key West still welcomed many visitors to the city, snowbirds from the north seeking refuge from the cold weather. Maria Popoff was adamant that something needed to be done soon while the world was still very much focused upon the chaos; destruction and heart break of the Ukrainian cities and its people. Finally, everyone settled upon Saturday March 19th because this would give the community just enough time to prepare. Pastor Joe offered to bring the church gospel choir to perform. Cora came up with the idea of a small springtime farm corner to keep the young children amused. She knew a farmer friend who had baby goats, chicks and ducklings and volunteered to talk with him and make the necessary arrangements. Bella and Harriet remembered seeing swathes of bright yellow and blue cotton stored away in an upstairs cupboard. Maria purchased them long ago at a fabric shop liquidation sale. The two elderly women had the bright idea of making pretty frocks from the 1950 - 1960's era in the colours of the Ukrainian national flag. Desmond shared that he'd noticed some Ukrainian women on the TV news broadcasts wearing garlands of flowers in their hair and thought that the community could make similar headpieces using silk spring flowers in their national colours. Maria agreed that this would be a wonderful idea and offered to drive to Miami where a large silk flower warehouse was located and purchase several boxes. Cora thought that Linda could get involved since she loved to keep her hands busy. This was going to be quite a project and everyone pitched in.

Over the next few days Cousin Rollo and Fred busied themselves in the gardens and approached the manager of a local hotel who kindly offered to not only loan but also agreed to erect their wedding marquee in the front garden ready for the March 19th festivities. Ruth and Betty put in extra hours in the kitchen making extra chocolate cake and fairy cakes with blue and yellow icing. Maria helped to create table decorations in the shape of a nest with little speckled blue candy eggs purchased from the local grocery store. St. Eustace quickly became a hive of activity and when some of the regular café customers learnt about the upcoming spring festival and how the community planned to raise funds for the Ukrainian refugees they offered to come in and help too.

It was in all this hive of activity and chaos that Desmond noticed a pile of sturdy black dustbin bags and an old battered cardboard box on the doorstep very early one morning as he arrived to open up for the day. He procured a steaming pot of coffee from the kitchen and sat in the still quietness of the early morning on the porch just as the sun was rising above the horizon. The sky turned crimson then gradually transformed into a delicate pink and finally into an eggshell blue. Yet another day in paradise was beginning. Listening intently to the birds chirping in the trees he reflected upon how very happy he felt. "I've found my niche here at St. Eustace," he muttered to Ruth's little dog, Henry, who'd joined him on the porch.

Having finished up his cup of coffee Desmond rifled through the black dustbin bags and saw that they were filled with a wide array of vintage clothes, shoes and straw hats. "Well, Maria will be pleased with this fancy treasure haul. Lots of expensive looking frocks here!" Then he carefully opened the old cardboard box and much to his surprise he saw a black enamel box about two and a half feet square with silver handles and brass hinges and a clasp. When Desmond gingerly opened the mysterious box, he saw an intricate contraption with three batteries, a tiny dynamo and intricate coils. He immediately realized that it was possibly a very old wireless probably from the very early 20th century.

Prior to the 1920's the radio was primarily used to contact ships that were out at sea. Radio communications were not very clear, so operators typically relied on the use of Morse code messages. This was of great benefit to vessels at sea especially during emergencies. However, all amateur and commercial use of radios came to an abrupt halt on April 7th, 1917 when the United States entered World War One. Most private U.S. radio stations were ordered by President Woodrow Wilson to either shut down or be taken over by the government. For the duration of the war, it became illegal for private U.S. citizens to even have an operational radio transmitter or receiver in fact it was treason to possess wireless stations. There was much fear in the United States about the radio being used for spying, much of it being baseless hysteria however, there were also legitimate concerns.

Desmond was intrigued by his discovery and wondered who could possibly have left it upon the doorstep of St. Eustace and why. He gently fingered all the intricate workings of the black box and shutting his eyes he drifted off to another time.

Frieda was eleven years old in 1907 when she made the long sea voyage with her family from the port of Bremen in Germany to New York. The immigrant family entered through Ellis Island along with 1.25 million immigrants passing through that particular year. In fact, 1907 proved to be Ellis Island's busiest year. The family came in search of a new life. They all breathed a sigh of relief as their steam ship passed the

Statue of Liberty hopeful of an exciting, prosperous future. They eventually headed west to Milwaukee in the Midwest to join distant relatives. Frieda's grandparents were promised the opportunity to purchase a small Wisconsin wheat and dairy farm and her father had been offered a well-paid factory job in the industrial city of Milwaukee.

It was a difficult beginning having left behind their homeland and unlike many others of Germanic descent Frieda and her close family found life in the polluted, busy city of Milwaukee inhospitable. Her parents were particularly reluctant to abandon their roots and move on in their new homeland. Frieda and her brothers easily became the target of bullies at school. Her father didn't get on with his co-workers at the heavy engineering factory where he worked and her mother, being rather portly and unattractive, found it very hard to make any new friends amongst the neighbourhood housewives. She felt increasingly lonely and isolated. As time went on the whole family became isolated and Frieda's parents deeply regretted ever making their long sea voyage to the USA. In Frieda's formative years her sole memory was of her parents often complaining and bitterly regretting ever moving to another country. Mother and father constantly reflected upon and talked about their previous life in Germany. Frieda and her brothers only ever heard the message that life was better in Germany. Subsequently they all lived more in the past and there was little room and opportunity for them to fully assimilate into their new surroundings.

The one saving grace for Frieda and her younger brothers was in the solace and happiness that they found at their grandparent's farm on the outskirts of Lake Mills in Wisconsin. The children spent their long school holidays there. She loved the little town of Lake Mills; it was small, clean and easy to get around. It was a complete, idyllic change of scenery from the hectic lifestyle and pollution of Milwaukee. There was a wonderful lake and swimming beach where they all spent many happy, lazy, sun filled hours in their early teenage years. Frieda and her brothers were a great help around the farm especially when it came to harvest time. Their grandparents also had a number of farm animals and Frieda loved to milk the cows, feed the chickens and gather in the newly laid eggs.

Grandpa absolutely loved to tinker. He built and mended things but his greatest interest and his most cherished possession was his Marconi radio. Guglielmo Marconi had developed, demonstrated and marketed the first successful long-distance wireless telegraph. Grandpa's prized radio was purchased in 1906 from Marconi's first wireless factory established in a former silk mill on Hall Street, Chelmsford, England in 1898. Marconi's Telegraph Company was founded a year later and the first transatlantic radio signal was broadcast in 1901.Grandpa spent much of his free evening time in his old barn fiddling with the radio and teaching Frieda and her brothers how to operate it. They all learnt and became very proficient in Morse code but Frieda was his star pupil and always remained the apple of his eye.

Frieda was 19 years old in 1915 when she moved to Key West. It seemed like the end of the world to leave behind her close-knit family and her younger brothers but she was a clever, spunky young woman, full of a sense for adventure. She absolutely hated her domestic housekeeping job in Milwaukee but when her current employer announced his transfer to far away Key West to work as a senior administrator at the Naval Station, she agreed to join his family there. She liked the idea of sunshine and warm weather in the wintertime and sandy beaches with gently swaying palm trees. It all conjured up an exotic, tempting image and certainly a far cry from the busy polluted streets of Milwaukee. Construction for Henry Flagler's East Coast Railroad had begun in 1905 and the first train to make the historic journey arrived on January 22nd 1912. Frieda was absolutely thrilled to make her own exciting and somewhat pioneering journey on Flagler's railroad in June of 1915.

Key West's Naval Station had strong historical roots. On March 25th 1822, Naval officer Matthew C. Perry sailed the schooner Shark to Key West and planted the U.S. flag claiming the Keys as United States property. The U.S. Government established an anti- pirate squadron at

Key West in December 1822 and a Naval Base was established a year later in what in current times is known as Mallory Square. Piracy in the Caribbean had been a big problem. Many American ships were lost so President Monroe authorized the establishment of an anti-pirate squadron. In 1860, illegal slavers were a serious problem and the federal government declared slave trading as piracy. Once again, the U.S. Navy was dispatched to Key West to patrol local waters and arrest American vessels taking part in the slave trade. Then with the start of the Civil War, the Navy organized a blockade squadron in Key West. Many ships patrolled from here to prevent the import of Confederate war supplies from overseas ports. Army troops assigned to Fort Zachary Taylor also boarded Navy transport ships and launched attacks into south Florida to cut off Confederate supply lines. Key West was the lone southern port that did not fall under Confederate control. The Union's strategic hold on Key West is said to have shortened the war by several years due to the South's inability to maintain open supply lines.

The Key West Naval Base was expanded further in the Spanish-American War. In 1898 the battleship Maine sailed from Key West to Cuba where it sank. The sinking of the Maine contributed to a U.S. declaration of war on Spain and the entire U.S. Atlantic Fleet moved to Key West for the duration of the war. After the war the active naval presence was withdrawn only to return again in World War 1. Year-round ideal weather for training and the island's strategic location led to the establishment of a navy submarine base at what is now Truman Annex. The Naval Base also proved to be an ideal training facility for the Navy's developing aviation force.

Frieda diligently undertook her domestic duties. Keeping house for her well-respected employer and his family was hard work. Florida was hot and humid during the summer time. Winters weren't so bad. Sunday was her one and only day off and she relished the opportunity to walk down to the sandy beach, bask in the sunshine and dip her toes in the warm clear blue waters gently lapping against the white sand. She liked to collect seashells then sit under a shady coconut palm tree and write letters home to her family back in Milwaukee and Lake Mills.

She met Hans, a young man in his early twenties, in January of 1917. He suddenly appeared on the beach early one Sunday morning collecting shells quite near to where she was sitting under a palm tree. Striking up a conversation and discovering their shared interest in sea shells and Germanic ancestry got the young couple off to a good start. Hans was well built, athletic, tanned and had a shock of light blond hair. With these strong Germanic features Frieda knew that her family would approve. He was also well educated and had travelled from New York in 1916 to work in Henry Flagler's East Coast Railroad Office.

Their friendship blossomed for many months, always on a Sunday as they shared the same day off from their respective work duties. They collected shells together, strolled along the beach and took tea at a local tearoom in the town. Hans talked animatedly about his large family. They too had passed through Ellis Island in 1907 but chose to make their home in New York City. Hans confided that his whole family also really missed their Germanic roots. His parents often talked about the old country. Leaving many friends and relatives behind to embark upon a new life in America hadn't been easy at all. In fact, *The Promised Land* wasn't quite as full of promise as they had anticipated. Over the years some altercations with very difficult neighbouring families in their crowded New York tenement blocks left his family seething with resentment upon a number of occasions. Of course, it wasn't good to bear grudges but Hans and his older brother Klaus found it difficult to forgive, forget and move on especially as they noticed their elderly parents growing more vulnerable and disillusioned with the choice that they'd so bravely made back in 1907.

Klaus was the real rebel in the family. He joined all kinds of political and very questionable organizations. His growing hatred of all things American was particularly disturbing to all those who knew him well. Hans often feared for his brother's safety. One day he confided in Frieda. "He's much too involved in nefarious political groups and one day I'm sure he'll get himself into a lot of trouble and maybe come to some harm."

When World War 1 erupted in Europe in 1914, President Woodrow Wilson pledged neutrality but tensions heightened in 1915 as Germany tried to isolate Britain and announced unrestricted attacks against all ships that entered the war zone around the British Isles. In early April 1917 as more and more U.S. merchant ships were sunk and civilian casualties were rising, President Wilson asked Congress for a war to end all wars that would make the world safe for democracy. So, on Friday April 6th 1917 Congress voted to declare war on Germany to protect shipping and the freedom of trade while in international waters.

Although America had ostensibly remained neutral until April 1917, in the early years of World War 1, as many as 1,000 American horses per day were shipped off to Europe to assist in the Allied war effort. Those horses became the target of germ warfare, infected with anthrax cultures on American soil. At the same time mysterious explosions were rocking U.S. munitions factories and fires were breaking out on ships headed to Europe. It was part of an aggressive campaign of spying and sabotage that the German government unleashed on America soon after the war began. For several years many German Americans struggled with their feelings, realizing that sympathy for their homeland appeared to conflict with loyalty to America. Fuel for the fire grew in places such as the New York waterfront. There were many taverns filled with Germans. Bored men concerned because many of their relatives were involved in fighting in Europe. They felt cut off, missed their homeland, missed the war, and it created a situation, in effect, a fifth column in America. Hans always suspected that his brother Klaus had become involved with some German terrorist cell. These were probably the mysterious people behind the growing number of sabotage incidents upon American soil and at sea.

When Frieda and Hans met on Sunday April 8th 1917 they had much to talk and anguish about. When World War 1 began in 1914 there'd been a backlash against German culture in America. Now that America was publicly at war with Germany the young couple feared possible physical attacks upon themselves, their parent's homes and their businesses. It was also the day that Frieda quite innocently shared with Hans her skills as a radio operator. Her grandparents had casually come up in conversation over tea and cake at their favourite cafe in town. She talked fondly of happier days, her early teenage years spent helping on the family farm on the outskirts of Lake Mills, Wisconsin. She talked about grandpa and his Marconi radio and how he'd taught them all how to use Morse code. "I'm really very proficient," she announced with a triumphant smile. "Grandpa passed his radio onto me as my parting gift when I was preparing to leave home and journey to Key West. He reluctantly shared with me that he was becoming too old and weary and couldn't remember a lot of things. He thought that his beloved radio would be safer and more useful in my capable hands." Hans threw back his head and laughed, "You really are quite a woman, Frieda, and every Sunday that passes I fall more and more in love with you!"

Thus far life was fairly comfortable for Hans. Currently he had a good job; he liked the Key West lifestyle; he was falling in love with a pretty young woman of Germanic descent and Europe was so very far away. Unlike Klaus, he'd never taken much interest in politics preferring a quiet lifestyle and minimal stress. Hans avoided confrontation. Life had been difficult for him in New York but unlike his older brother he tended to sweep his anger under the carpet and put on a silent smiling face. However, deep beneath the surface his anger and resentment simmered and waited for the day that the inevitable big bang would surely happen.

Hans clearly recalled the day in mid-June 1917 when Klaus came knocking at his door. It had been a beautiful, idyllic and sunny day; strolling along the beach in the early evening after work at the railroad office he'd thought about asking Frieda to marry him. The war seemed so very far away. Key West, situated at the end of the road, seemed so very far removed from the battlefields of Flanders. Hans prepared himself a simple supper of bread and cheese at his rooming house then he read the newspaper. However, as it became late and he was preparing to retire for the night, he suddenly heard a loud, sharp, urgent rap at his door. "Hans, it's me open up, quickly!"

Klaus stumbled across the threshold. Hans could see that his leg was injured, his trousers were slightly torn at the knee and he noticed congealed blood underneath the torn cloth. Limping over to a chair by the window Klaus collapsed with a weary sigh. Unshaven, dishevelled and looking as if he hadn't slept for days Hans anxiously wondered how he'd made it to his door and what sort of trouble his brother had got himself into. He rushed to bring him some water and hastily put together a plate of bread and cheese. Luckily the rooming house was quiet as most of the occupants were already in bed and asleep. Hans ran downstairs to the communal kitchen. Thankfully it was deserted. He breathed a sigh of relief because he wouldn't have to face a barrage of questions from some of the more curious tenants. He heated water on the wood stove, gathered clean cloth from the washhouse and headed upstairs. Having grabbed Lugol's iodine solution and bandages from his dresser drawer to tend to his brother's gaping wound he set to work. When Klaus was feeling more comfortable, he began to tell his story. Hans pulled up a chair and listened intently.

"Hans I'm in big trouble. The Bureau of Investigation is after me. I had to get out of New York quickly and find somewhere to hide. Key West, being so far away and at the end of the road, seemed to be the perfect solution especially since my younger brother resides in the town. To make a long story short I've been involved with a German terrorist cell for several years now. When the war started, I couldn't bring myself to simply sit back and do nothing. I love my homeland too much and for as long as I can remember I've been sick and tired of the way we were all treated growing up in Milwaukee. I was sick of being an outsider, ostracized for our language and customs, bullied at school and at work too. The feelings of injustice and resentment are deep rooted and have compelled me to act rather than sit back like so many other folk who simply talk. I'm a man of action and of course it's got me into big trouble. However, Hans just know that I don't have any regrets, truthfully my heart is hard and full of hatred but I don't want to pull you into my affairs and cause you or the rest of our family problems. I know that you follow a different path so it's best that you're kept in the dark and that I don't share details of my involvement with this cell. The bottom line is that I cannot stay here in America. I've burnt all my bridges. Hans, if by chance I'm caught, I could face the death sentence or life imprisonment. Right now, it's expedient that I get out and make my way to Germany. I know that there are German U-boats in this area and my intelligence sources tell me that if I'm able to make contact with one of them and if a rendezvous can be arranged that I would be guaranteed safe passage to Germany. There's no coming back Hans. Once I leave, you'll probably never hear or see from me again. Just know that I'm a man of conviction and once I make up my mind, I always see things through. Of course, I'll miss my family but it's the path I've chosen and now I have to face the consequences. Will you please shelter me for a few days?"

Hans didn't know what to say. His brother was already in his home. He'd offered him assistance. Hans knew that sheltering a criminal, a terrorist at that, was wrong and would cause extremely serious repercussions if these things ever came to light. However, Klaus was his brother, his own flesh and blood and he felt a strong brotherly duty at the very least to help him get away. He just couldn't find the courage within himself to simply turn his back and hand him over to the police. Hans took a deep breath and said, "Klaus, it's far too dangerous to stay here, there's many idle folk with prying eyes, tenants who pass away their days peering behind lace curtains and they tend to ask too many questions. Best that we leave right now under the cover of darkness. I can take you over to the Flagler rail sheds. There are a couple of older railroad carriages in for repair but they aren't on the work schedule for at least a few months. No one will bother to look for you there."

Hans brought his brother a change of clothes and hastily put together a knapsack for him with extra clean bandages, Lugol's iodine solution, a blanket, a change of clothes, some tinned food and bottled water that would see him through for a few days. Leaving at 1 o'clock under the cover of darkness and with Klaus limping badly they very slowly made their way across the main town to the rail sheds.

Once settled in the relative comfort of a Flagler passenger rail carriage Hans confided that the young lady who he happened to be stepping out with had a Marconi radio in her possession and was a skilled Morse code operator. Klaus smiled with surprise and relief because suddenly his future looked even brighter and more secure. "Hans, give me a piece of paper and a pencil. I'm going to give you the name, address and radio contact of a trusted person. This is someone high up who will never divulge your identity. They can be contacted through the Marconi radio and will facilitate getting me safely onto a German submarine plying the waters off Key West."

It was going to be far too risky to ever be seen together so Hans told his brother that he would put together a small pack of food and water each day, dropping it off at sunset and that it would be hidden behind some large boulders at the entrance to the rail sheds. He would leave any important messages tucked inside a loaf of bread. Klaus was instructed to venture out only when it was dark and when everyone had retired for the night.

Hans embraced his brother knowing that this would probably be their last goodbye. Leaving him behind in the safety of the rail shed and the scribbled note tucked away in his pocket he hurried back to his rooming house. It was fast approaching 4 o'clock. He would have a few hours in bed before the sun came up and the beginning of yet another busy day at The Flagler Railroad Office. Frieda was on his mind as he mumbled the same question to himself many times, "How on earth am I going to persuade Frieda to send a Morse code message to the hastily scribbled name in my pocket?" This was the most difficult night of his life but eventually he fell into a restless slumber.

Friday was, as predicted, a busy day at work and there was little time for Hans to reflect upon the strange happenings of the previous night. That evening as he strolled along the beach at sunset, he deliberated with himself how he could possibly approach Frieda on their regular Sunday outings. Part of him didn't want to draw her into this awful mess but he knew that if his brother were caught, he would probably face the death sentence. On Saturday evening, just as darkness was drawing in, he discreetly left a small parcel of food and some glass bottles filled with water behind the large boulders by the rail shed. Hans wondered how his brother was doing. He wondered if he was suffering any adverse symptoms from his gaping knee wound, perhaps a fever had set in? However, he knew that he couldn't risk ever being seen with his brother again.

Hans arrived at the beach early on Sunday morning. He'd already spent several hours sitting under a palm tree in deep thought when Frieda arrived. As she sat down beside him, she immediately felt that something was wrong. She'd come to know Hans very well and intuitively she sensed that he was anguishing over a big problem. Having spent a few minutes greeting each other and exchanging some genteel small talk she decided that it was best to come straight to the point. Much to his surprise and speaking with authority Frieda said, "Hans you are so very troubled, it's written all over your face and body. Please be honest with me and tell me what's happened. I want to help. Is it your job or your health? Your family? Are they all OK?"

Hans took a deep breath and decided then and there that the only way forward was to be completely honest with Frieda. So, for the best part of an hour, he told her all about his brother and his present predicament down to the very last detail. Then he pulled out the scribbled note from his pocket and looking directly into her eyes he said, "I have to ask you to make radio contact with this person, they can arrange a U-boat pick up for Klaus and whisk him away to Germany. I don't know any other way to contact this person and Frieda you 're the only person I know who actually owns a radio and can use Morse code. Please, please say yes!"

This strange and dangerous request was indeed an extremely tall order and took Frieda completely by surprise; in fact, she was dumb struck.

This was a lot to ask and if she were caught, she could be tried with treason. On the other hand, she had both the skills and the necessary equipment and she loved Hans with all of her heart. Once she gathered her composure, she pressed Hans to answer the one question that rested heavily upon her young shoulders, "Hans, will you abandon me if I say no? Will that be the end of us?"

Taken aback Hans sighed and said; "Of course not Frieda but I don't know how I could possibly live with myself if I didn't help Klaus to safety. His imprisonment or death would weigh heavily upon my shoulders. I think that my guilty feelings would eat away at me like an acid and in time it might destroy the man that I am. I may turn into someone so difficult to live with that eventually it would break us apart. My brother's chosen path has thrown us two innocent young lovers into the dark, dangerous, nefarious world of terrorists."

Neither Hans nor Frieda felt good about the situation. Eventually after much thought Frieda said, "Hans I'll make only one attempt to contact the name scribbled on this piece of paper. I'll make that very clear in my message to this person. I'll also tell them that they are to answer my call only once with the date and the time of a rendezvous meeting for Klaus. I'll tell them that I'll only listen in for an answer every night between midnight and 2 o'clock for seven nights following that initial contact call. Then I'll pack up my Marconi radio and hide it away in the attic of my employers' big house. Hans, I probably won't ever touch my grandfather's beloved radio again because what you've asked of me is against my nature. I must confess that I love you very much and my heart tells me not to let you down. Love wins today Hans but always know that my heart will remain forever heavy with guilt because I'll, in the eyes of America, always be seen as a traitor."

At the beginning of World War 1 few Americans believed that German U-boats would be able to transverse the Atlantic to reach American shores, but they were wrong and by the end of the World War 1, four German submarines visiting the east coast had managed to sink 10 vessels off North Carolina alone, and 200 American ships in total. The

German U-boats were quite advanced and generally painted a dull dirty grey colour. They were 210 - 225 feet long, 20 - 22 feet in breadth and could draw approx. 12 feet of water. They carried 25 men and 12 torpedoes. The U-boats could reach maximum depths of 50 meters or 165 feet; achieve speeds averaging 16 knots at the surface and 8 knots underwater. They were able to travel underwater for up to two hours at a time if operating at a slow speed and were armed with deck-mounted guns.

Frieda was as good as her word. She was most uncomfortable with the plan hatched by Klaus and supported by Hans and was very wary of the dangerous and risky situation that she was personally exposing herself to. However, she'd made a promise and had no intention of letting her darling Hans down. Frieda knew that the most dangerous time would be when she transmitted from her Marconi radio; this was the only time that she could actually be traced. "Thank goodness I agreed to do this only once," she muttered to herself when she'd returned to the large home where she worked. Frieda pulled the black enamel box with silver handles and brass hinges housing her Marconi radio out from under her bed. She opened it up and checked the three batteries and the connections then she looked at the calendar to determine the phases of the moon during the next few weeks. Thankfully there was a new moon on Tuesday June 19th just a couple of nights away. She was relieved because she desperately wanted to get this mission over and done by quickly and this would surely be the best night to transmit her message under the cover of relative darkness.

It was still very light outside so she decided to take a brisk walk over to the Key West Cemetery in the heart of Old Town and at the foot of Solares Hill. It was established in 1847, after the hurricane of October 1846 destroyed and washed away several burial grounds throughout the island. The Key West Cemetery was the final resting place of so many interesting, adventurous and quirky folk who'd all eked out a living at one time or other in the city at the end of the road. Ghost stories abounded and Frieda knew that many local residents wouldn't venture through the cemetery gates after darkness fell. It was situated on relatively high ground and seemed to be an ideal, secretive place where she could safely transmit and avoid detection.

It was a lovely warm June evening and Frieda enjoyed a leisurely stroll around the cemetery. Finally, she spotted a large family memorial vault not far from the memorial to the U.S. Battleship Maine, erected as a tribute to the disastrous sinking of the battleship in Havana Harbour on February 15th 1898. The large family vault was in a poor state of disrepair. It was overgrown with weeds and some old straggling cactus plants. Frieda noticed a large gaping hole where some of the stone had eroded and broken up. It was big enough to slide her Marconi radio down into the dark recess and store it after her first transmission. Frieda chuckled to herself, "I can hide it safely there and it will be waiting for me when I return each night between midnight and 2 o'clock to listen in for a response to my transmission to this mysterious person."

She returned home and ventured up into the attic. Everyone else in the household had retired to bed. Frieda searched around for a suitable hiding place for her beloved radio once her dirty work was over. She also spotted a large oilskin cloth that would help to keep her radio safe and dry in its hiding place at the cemetery. Gathering up the oilskin she crept downstairs and fell into bed. Sunday June 17th had been so exhausting physically, mentally and emotionally. She questioned herself as she fell into a restless slumber. "Frieda, what on earth have you got yourself into?"

As carefully planned, she ventured out at midnight on Tuesday. It had been a cloudy, rainy day and the sky was thankfully an inky black. The streets of Old Town were deserted. Clutching the radio carefully wrapped in the oilskin cloth tightly to her chest she hurried along. It was cumbersome and heavy and she felt thankful that she'd found a hiding place for it at the cemetery. Entering through the gates she took a very deep breath and muttered to herself, "Frieda put on your big girl pants and take courage! Ignore the dark shadows and those scary tales of ghost stories and just set to. Get this job done!" She quickly reached the old family vault that she'd earmarked on Sunday evening. Carefully scanning her surroundings to ensure there was no one else around she hurriedly unwrapped the radio opened it up and began to set the antenna up. She'd rehearsed many times in her head the brief Morse code message to be transmitted to the mysterious name and call signal hastily scribbled on the piece of paper she'd pulled out of her pocket.

Urgent. Klaus is in eminent danger. U-boat rendezvous required from Key West with safe passage to Germany. Require date, time and location of rendezvous. Listening in between midnight and 2 o'clock for next 7 nights only. No more transmissions possible.
Too dangerous.

Frieda breathed a sigh of relief as she packed her radio away and carefully wrapped it in the oilskin cloth. Her heart was still pounding as she slid it down into the dark hole of the family vault. She plucked a handful of weeds from adjoining gravesites and piled them around the recess area so everything was completely hidden. She couldn't wait to get out of the cemetery. She felt exhausted, frightened and extremely anxious that someone may have seen or heard her. However, as she set off home the cemetery remained silent except for the sound of the nocturnal mole crickets. Her heart palpitations finally settled down as she fell into bed. Glancing at her bedside clock she noticed that it was a little past 1 o'clock. Sighing, she hoped that a message would come back soon so that she'd be done with this sordid business.

It was Friday night when a brief message was finally received. Frieda breathed a sigh of relief. This meant that she could return home with her Marconi radio and forget her part in this act of treason.

Midnight. Sunday June 24th. Key West Southern Point Beach. Small fishing boat - The Victory - passenger rendezvous. If weather very bad - midnight Wednesday June 27th

Frieda hurriedly packed up her radio, wrapped it in the oilskin cloth and made her way towards the cemetery gates. It was almost 2 o'clock. Suddenly startled she caught a glimpse of an old tramp, whisky bottle in hand, bellowing at her, "Who goes there? Only the dead ghouls walk here in the darkness of the night. Show yourself!" Frieda didn't stop she broke into a sprint to get away from the drunk old man. She felt her heart pounding against the heavy enamel casing of her radio as she clutched it close to herself. Thankfully the streets were deserted as she made her way to the elegant home on Caroline Street where she lived and worked.

The next day cook sent her out to the local market to purchase vegetables and fruit for a fancy dinner that she was preparing. "The household is entertaining this evening because important visitors are in town. Mind you hurry back girl and help me out in the kitchen today." Frieda used this opportunity to quickly slip away to the Flagler Railroad Office where Hans was sitting studiously behind a large oak desk working on a pile of papers. He looked up in surprise; Frieda had never visited him at his place of work before. She quickly handed him the piece of notepaper upon which she'd carefully recorded the message she'd received the night before. Frieda smiled and whispered, "mission accomplished! I look forward to seeing you on Sunday as usual." Before Hans had time to speak, she'd swiftly made her way out of the door and was heading over towards the market.

It took Frieda a very long time to recover from the events of mid-June 1917. Although their mission was complete the events that she'd become involved in played out in her mind for many months and in the years to come they would recur frequently when she was feeling particularly low and vulnerable. She felt guilty because what she'd become part of didn't sit well with her conscience at all. Hans wasn't much better; he was a sensitive soul too and as time went on, he became quite angry with this brother because his actions had put them both at risk and in such an impossible situation.

Hans had visited Klaus at the Flagler rail sheds one last time very late in the evening of Saturday June 23rd. His brother's knee injury was healing nicely and he was looking rested and so much better compared to their first encounter at his rooming house. Hans handed him Frieda's note and wished him a safe passage. Klaus smiled and simply said, "Yes, the fishing boat will take me out to sea and rendezvous with the German U-boat. Many thanks, Hans, and please thank Frieda too. I won't be troubling you ever again."

Klaus was as good as his word. Hans never heard from him again. He assumed that his brother made the rendezvous and arrived safely in Germany because Sunday June 24th had been an idyllic day. The weather was good and the seas were calm. That same day Frieda climbed the stairs up to the attic and carefully placed her Marconi radio into a sturdy cardboard box. She ran her fingers lovingly over the enamel black casing one last time as tears rolled down her cheeks. She muttered to herself, "Grandpa will be so very disappointed in me. He loved and cherished this radio. He trusted it to me for safekeeping. It was intended for my future enjoyment but now I feel that I can't ever use it again. It's become tainted by my actions these past few days! Hopefully others will find it sometime in the future and love it as much as our family did. I hope that it can have a fresh start with someone else so much worthier than I am."

Frieda slowly made her way down the attic stairs. Her shoulders were stooped; her head hung low and her heart felt particularly heavy. The radio was left behind when Hans and Frieda finally left Key West. They married in 1919. The war was over; he'd been offered a senior office position with the Flagler East Coast Railway up in St. Augustine, Florida. Frieda secured a job in the city's fancy luxury Hotel Ponce de Leon that had opened in 1888 and was also built by Henry Flagler.

The elegant home on Caroline Street remained in the same family for well over a hundred years and Frieda's Marconi radio in its black enamel casing remained silent and hidden for all those years too. However, in 2021 during the Corona Virus crisis, the valuable property was listed for sale and spotted by Trudy and Doug. They were a wealthy, glamorous hipster couple living in New York but looking for an investment opportunity in Key West. The couple had plans to turn it into a fancy Bed and Breakfast establishment.

When the sale was completed a well-known local building firm were contracted to make improvements, decorate and clear the attic of all the bric-a-brac accumulated over the years. Tony was a carpenter working on the renovation project. He happened to be on hand during the day when the attic was cleared and Frieda's radio was discovered. No one working at the home really knew exactly what it was or its significance. Tony recalled how his wife like to shop for vintage clothes at nearby St. Eustace and thought that it could be taken there along with the large pile of old frocks, shoes and straw hats they'd cleared out. "Shame to throw that stuff on the bonfire! Someone might find a use for it all. That strange old woman, Maria Popoff, seems to run the place. My wife likes her lot. She's a regular customer at the porch café that they set up. Apparently, they serve great chocolate cake! Perhaps the old woman can pass some of this stuff along, find a new owner. Let's load up my truck lads and I'll drop it off on my way home tonight."

Desmond opened his eyes; his fingers ran lightly over the black enamel casing and tears ran down his cheeks. Henry stirred and came over to lick his face just as Maria arrived on the porch her coffee cup in hand. It wasn't necessary for Maria to ask questions. Her beady eyes glanced at the piles of black dustbin bags and then they rested upon the black casing and she knew immediately that it was an ancient Marconi radio. Placing her coffee cup on a nearby table she sat down next to Desmond and gently put her right arm around his shoulders. During their shared silence her left hand ran over the box, she sighed and eventually after sometime had passed she began to speak.

"Desmond it's difficult being human. No one said that life on earth was going to be easy. Our lives are but one day in school. We all come to learn and to grow spiritually; some of us are much better at it than others. The clocks tick, time passes and we only have so long to make the minutes count. I believe that we have many lifetimes and in each one we learn important life lessons. Love is the most important thing, to love others, lend a helping hand, treat people with respect, be grateful for what we have and to walk a path that feels good for our soul. There's a sad story connected with this radio and I can see that it deeply touched your soul too. When we do things against our own inner compass usually trouble sets in. Klaus put his brother and Frieda in an impossible situation and the choice they both made affected them for the rest of their lives. It was costly. Frieda suffered many illnesses because she was so troubled by her past. She couldn't let go of what she'd done; the guilt haunted her until her dying day. Hans suffered too; he experienced fits of dark, all-encompassing depression and took to drinking far too much to silence the constant chatter and anguish in his mind.

There was a young English doctor called Edward Bach busily working at the same time that Hans and Frieda were living out their own life story. He was a sensitive soul too. Due to his own bad health, he wasn't strong enough to go to France and fight but he was in charge of over 400 surgical wartime beds in a famous London Hospital. He studied his patients carefully and wanted to fully understand their illnesses and why so many never got better. His close scrutiny and observations eventually taught him that following the dictates of our soul and finding balance in our emotional state is the key to good health and happiness. Later in his life he found what he called the *38 superior healers of mankind.* They are known as the Bach flower essences although one of them is made from the water of an ancient holy stream. The essences are gentle helpers. They can assist us when we stray from walking our true path. They cover the whole gambit of human emotions from trauma, terror, fear, anger and bitterness to loss, grief, depression and despair to indecision, apathy and guilt. Desmond you would do well to read about Dr. Bach and his essences. Do find the time. You could help many customers who often come to us for more than our vintage paraphernalia, tea and chocolate cake.

Both Hans and Frieda's family became too stuck in the past. They found it difficult to shake off their Germanic roots and truly settle in America. When one lives too much in the past then the Bach essence *Honeysuckle* can be very helpful. It's a flower that helps people to move on and to find meaning and joy in their present circumstances rather than remain too stuck in a past that's always perceived as being much better than the present. The families were also weighed down by much bitterness, anger and resentment. *Bach Holly* is a good essence for raw explosive anger and jealousy too. *Willow,* on the other hand, is an excellent essence to consider when anger becomes colder. It's for anger that's become deeper rooted and eats away like an acid destroying all thoughts of kindness, goodness and love. *Bach Willow* is for people consumed by bitterness, self-pity and resentment. Their hearts have become heavy, they bear grudges and there's little room for joy. Then there's *Bach Pine* a wonderful remedy to help those who feel burdened by too much guilt. Whether they are at fault or it's someone else, they blame themselves, pull themselves down and feel unworthy."

Desmond dried his eyes and looked up at Maria Popoff. Behind all the wrinkled skin and piercing blue eyes he saw what a uniquely wise, generous, loving person she truly was. "Thank you for being such a wonderful mentor, for gracing my life and teaching me so much. So, what do you think we should do with this old radio?"

Before Maria had time to answer Linda arrived with a feather duster in hand. She was collecting the tea and coffee cups but her eye caught the black enamel box resting on Desmond's knees and before anyone had time to stop her, she'd picked it up with her busy fingers itching to open the clasps and explore further. Much to everyone's astonishment she quite suddenly pushed it quickly away as if it were a hot plate. Looking directly at Desmond and Maria, she took them completely by surprise when she exclaimed, "No, too sad, go away!" Maria turned to Desmond and simply said, "Linda is sensitive and all-knowing just like us. Linda is one of us. This radio is a museum piece and it can't be passed on. Sadly, it's the receptacle of far too much emotional baggage. Desmond, sometimes we receive things that can't be passed on. Nevertheless, it's a valuable part of our history and so well preserved. Certainly, it's not right to take it to the back of the house and destroy it on the bonfire. I think that we could create a museum case celebrating Key West and its history. We could start off with the sponge pole, add this Marconi radio and in time other things will find a new home here at St. Eustace."

Linda took off muttering to herself, "Linda's one of us." Although she'd spoken one or two words beforehand the Marconi radio encounter was the start of something exciting not only for Linda but for the whole St. Eustace community who'd come to love and cherish her. For the first time in her life, she felt included when she'd heard Maria speak those life-changing words, "Linda's one of us." She felt she was a normal person and no longer an outsider.

Bella and Harriet often sang songs as they busied themselves in the sewing room. Linda liked to hang out with them and they often set her to work cutting the brightly coloured cloth around the paper patterns for their vintage creations. After the radio encounter Linda suddenly began to join in and sing with the two elderly women as they worked on their sewing projects. The constant repetition of singing began to set her upon a new path of learning language and finding both the courage and the confidence to use her voice. By the time the much-anticipated spring festival came around on March 19th Linda was at long last able to greet visitors with a few words and speak in very simple sentences to engage with the customers in the café. Everyone celebrated including many of the regulars who'd become used to Linda's silence and her quirky busy ways.

The spring festival was a huge success and people generously donated. Maria had identified a Ukrainian church congregation who were sending much needed financial aid to their contacts in the war-torn country and helping the refugees. They were particularly grateful for the large donation that the St. Eustace community was able to send after their spring festival fundraising event.

Following on from the successful festival Fred suggested that the St. Eustace community organize an egg hunt in the gardens for the children on Easter Sunday afternoon. Everyone thought that was a wonderful idea. Harriet and Bella said that there was much talk in their church community about helping some refugee families so it was agreed with Pastor Joe that St. Eustace would support their mission with a special Eastertide project. Cora noticed lots of gaily coloured plastic eggs on display in the local hobby craft shops. She agreed to purchase several boxes and donate them to the project. They would be filled with little chocolate eggs purchased with some of the café profits. Cora also purchased and donated a number of decorative nests and bags of little blue speckled eggs from the hobby craft shops to create centrepieces for the dining tables. Fred asked Linda to help him fill the plastic eggs and asked if she would help him hide the eggs around the large gardens early on Easter Sunday morning. Ruth and Betty busily planned a special Easter afternoon tea party in the elegant dining room and out on the porch. Maria placed adverts in the local paper and glossy magazines. St. Eustace was really beginning to make a name for itself amongst the locals and visitors alike as a popular welcoming venue always with a mission to bring people together and to help others in need.

The daily lunchtime soup kitchen was a Godsend for the homeless community and Ruth's divine chocolate cake had quickly become the talk of the town. Afternoon tea on the porch was always fully booked and the families who visited the café enjoyed browsing in the quirky vintage shop Desmond and Maria had created.

As Putin's war in the Ukraine raged on making daily headlines in the news media Maria continued to restlessly pace the empty, silent corridors of St. Eustace late at night deeply troubled by the civilian atrocities in Bucha and the constant bombardment of Mariupol. There was much talk about war crimes being committed. She earnestly prayed for peace sending Putin and his supporters the energy of *Holly*, the Bach flower that opens up the heart, dissolves hatred and lets in love. In her anguish she often recalled the words of Dr. Edward Bach:

"Holly protects us from everything that is not universal love If we have in our nature sufficient love of all things, then we can do no harm; because that love would stay our hand at any action, our mind at any thought which might hurt another."

Buried Treasure

Easter Sunday came around all too quickly. Linda woke up early eagerly anticipating the fun filled day. She knew that Fred wanted her to help him hide the eggs so Cora set her alarm clock for 6 am and was already down in the kitchen cooking breakfast when Linda burst in happily singing. Cora smiled and chuckled quietly to herself, "I never thought I'd see the day when my Linda could speak and be happy. Thank God for St. Eustace! The old house and its loving community have completely transformed our lives. I'm beginning to think that angels really do exist!"

Mother and daughter made their way quickly over to St. Eustace, where Fred was waiting on the porch with Desmond. The two young men had become firm friends and were in deep conversation when Linda arrived. She impatiently tugged at Fred's shirt exclaiming, "Let's go Fred, eggs waiting!" Fred put down his coffee mug and the two set off into the gardens to hide the brightly coloured plastic eggs filled with chocolate. Fred gave her strict instructions not to bury the eggs too deeply because the children would never find them and to please try and hide them in shady places under the trees and bushes because the hot sun would melt the eggs by the afternoon. They both set to work and were almost finished when Linda gave out a sudden yelp. Fred rushed across the garden towards her thinking that she'd hurt herself in some way. He was most surprised to see her hands covered in dirt and Linda peering down into a huge deep hole that had opened up under the gigantic monkey-puzzle tree. The tree was very old and probably at least 40 metres high.

Fred peered down into the gaping hole too. Linda didn't have the words to explain exactly what had happened but Fred guessed that some animal had been burrowing away and with Linda's poking around for egg hiding places and some recent heavy rainfall the hole had suddenly opened up. Fred lay down on his stomach and gingerly bent over the large gaping hole and carefully reached his long arms down towards some dark object that he could just about make out at the bottom. It appeared to be a chest of some sort. He turned to Linda and told her to quickly fetch Desmond to help and to bring a big spade from the garages. Desmond really didn't understand what Linda was trying to tell him but by the look on her face and her muddy hands he knew it was urgent. The only word he could make out was spade so he called to Bella who just happened to stop by to pick something up from the sewing room before church. "Bella please mind the vintage shop while I attend to some emergency situation out in the gardens!" Bella gasped in surprise as he quickly ran off with a very flustered looking Linda.

By the time that Desmond picked up the garden spade from the garages and arrived with Linda, who continued to look very flustered and perplexed, they were both astonished to see Fred was actually in the huge gaping hole. He was standing up and gazing high above to where they had gathered. Linda was dispatched yet again to find Cousin Rollo and get him to bring a ladder so that Fred could actually climb out of the hole. Desmond threw the garden spade down and Fred began to dig in earnest and after a short while he had prized free a particularly heavy hardwood chest from its resting place. It had an old rusty lock but it seemed impossible to open it up and see exactly what lay inside. Desmond shouted down to Fred, "We'll need to haul that up with some ropes I'll go to the garages to see what I can find." Cousin Rollo arrived in due course with the ladder and accompanied by Linda who still remained flustered and very worried when she still saw Fred deep down at the bottom of the hole. Cousin Rollo turned to Linda and in a calm, soothing voice he said, "Don't worry Linda we'll have Fred out of there in no time. We'll haul the big box up with ropes and we'll have to put tape around the area and have someone on guard today to make sure the children don't come near and fall down the hole during their egg hunt."

It was quite the calamity and certainly not the start to Easter Sunday that everyone had anticipated. With much huffing and puffing and some help from some of the regulars at the porch cafe who'd stopped by early for their morning coffee and freshly baked croissants, the chest was eventually hauled to the surface and taken into St. Eustace for closer examination. Of course, there was much speculation. Maria came downstairs to find out what all the commotion was in aid of. Linda simply pointed and excitedly yelled out, "treasure chest!" Maria smiled, "perhaps." Bella offered to return with Harriet after church to sit in the garden during the egg hunt ensuring that no one came near the hole and fell in. Cousin Rollo returned to the garages to find his roll of police incident tape and to make signs to warn folk of the imminent danger. The old muddy chest was set to rest behind the main counter in the vintage shop and hidden away from curious eyes. It was waiting for further examination but only when the time was right. Maria spoke with authority, "We'll have a very busy day ahead of us. A lot of visitors are expected and all the children will be here at 2pm for the egg hunt. Then there's the special afternoon tea that Ruth has laid on. Today we'll all forget about the chest but tomorrow we'll see if we can open it and discover what mysteries lie within!"

The Easter celebrations were a huge success. St. Eustace had managed to draw quite a crowd. The large grounds were the perfect location for the easter egg hunt. Squeals of delighted children could be heard up by the road and they enticed curious passers-by to walk through the gates and investigate for themselves what was happening at the large old house and in the gardens. Under Harriet and Bella's ever watchful eyes no one was allowed to venture near the mysterious hole. People donated generously when they learnt that all profits would be donated to helping Ukrainian refugees. As Maria locked up that night she smiled and felt in her heart that their little community was gently flourishing, gradually growing and truly making a difference. As she climbed the stairs to retire for the night, she muttered to herself, "St. Eustace is beginning to touch so many lives, I'm so glad that Cousin Rollo summoned me here to this quirky place at the end of the road!"

The next day Linda was up early, she made Cora a cup of tea and impatiently woke her mother even before the sun was up. "Treasure, time for treasure, let's go!" Cora stirred and smiled as she reflected that before St. Eustace her daughter had been mute and now, she couldn't find it within herself to scold Linda for waking her up so very early.

She quickly got out of bed, dressed, drank her tea and hurried out of the door with Linda who by now was beside herself with excitement. When they arrived at St. Eustace Cora was surprised to see how everyone else had exactly the same idea. Desmond and Fred were sitting on the front porch with Ruth drinking coffee and just as Cousin Rollo appeared Pastor Joe also pulled up in the old yellow school bus with Harriet and Bella. Fred exclaimed, "Ladies you're so very early today. I've never seen you arrive before 10am before!" Harriet and Bella smiled and nodded as Pastor Joe graciously took their hands and helped the elderly women up the steps onto the porch. "We've come to see the treasure and it looks like everyone else has the same idea!" With all the commotion on the front porch Maria appeared at the top of the stairs. Linda impatiently hopped from one foot to another and all eyes turned to Maria in anticipation that she would quickly begin proceedings.

The heavy old chest was pulled from its hiding place under the counter. Fred had brought a selection of tools up from the garages. Everyone gathered around with baited breath as Fred and Cousin Rollo fiddled for what felt like an eternity attempting to break the lock using a variety of tools. Eventually they were able to prise the rusty lock open. Fred peered down into the dark recess and sighed with disappointment because at first glance the treasure chest seemed empty. Then he suddenly pointed out something to Cousin Rollo and both men felt down at the bottom of the chest and gently lifted a small box wrapped in oilskin cloth. The curious crowd gathered closer as Fred gently unwrapped the cloth to reveal what looked remarkably like a cigar box. Maria reached out her hand and gently ran it over the box and exclaimed, "Spanish Cedar! Look at its attractive even-coloured grain. It's a hard wood coming from the same family as mahogany and isn't Spanish at all. It's durable and resistant to decay." The fascinated onlookers could see a dark reddish-brown box with a purplish tinge but because it was so old and hidden for so long it wasn't possible to discern any of the faded markings except the words:

Los mejores puros de Pedro

Cousin Rollo chuckled, "I think that says Pedro's finest cigars!" Linda was beside herself hopping from one foot to another. Maria kindly turned to her and said, "Linda come and gently open the box and show us all what's inside." Linda gingerly took the box from Fred's hands and lifted it open. She pulled out a black velvet pouch tied firmly at the top with a silk ribbon and as she undid the ribbon a small parcel wrapped in faded tissue paper fell out. Everyone gasped with baited breath as Linda's busy fingers unfolded the tissue paper to reveal a number of shiny gold coins. "Oh my!" exclaimed Maria, "I do believe that these might possibly be Spanish doubloons! They feel like solid gold and were widely used as currency in Spain and in the Spanish-colonies through the mid-1800's. These coins were also common in the American South, a region formerly occupied by Spain. However, they were largely banned as legal tender in the United States by 1860." As Maria spoke Linda counted seven gold coins and was quite beside herself with excitement interrupting and yelling over and over again, "treasure!"

Marie smiled, "Linda we did indeed find treasure. I'm not sure who this treasure belongs to but I'm sure that in time all will be revealed." The excitement of seeing so many gold coins had captured everyone's attention and it was Fred who finally noticed in all the commotion that there was a slip of paper discreetly tucked away in the cigar box. Fred couldn't read Spanish but he knew that Ruth could help as her worldly travels had taken her to Mexico many times. He carefully passed the frail piece of paper over to her.

Yo, Pedro, he hecho muchas cosas malas. He cometido errores y lo siento. Ojalá pudiera empezar de nuevo, pero es demasiado tarde. Ahora soy un hombre viejo y muy enfermo. Lo que queda de mi fortuna está enterrado aquí. Ojalá algún día se encuentre y que quien lo encuentre destine lo que queda a un buen fin, a algo noble. Por favor deja que este tesoro marque la diferencia.

The writing was somewhat faded but Ruth just about worked out what was being conveyed and began to read to everyone gathered around the empty chest and the bag of seven gold coins.

I, Pedro have done many bad things. I've made mistakes and I'm sorry. I wish that I could begin again but it's too late. I'm an old very sick man now. What's left of my fortune is buried here. I hope one day it is found and that the finder puts what's left towards a good purpose, something noble. Please let this treasure make a difference.

Everyone gasped then silently began to ponder over the significance of the faded note. Pastor Joe was the first one to break the awkward silence. "We must all pray for the soul of this man and ensure that his dying wishes are honoured." Maria looked around at her little band of helpers, the very people who'd brought life to St. Eustace. The thrill and joyous anticipation of buried treasure had quickly disappeared and their faces looked sad and drained. The wise old woman simply said, "Pedro's treasure may have been his downfall, it may be tainted and stained but, in the end, he knew that what remained needed to be used for a far nobler purpose and that's really important. Pedro finally saw the light. The St. Eustace community will ensure that his wishes are carried out, after all he buried it on our property, we are its guardians and with new found wealth we'll make the difference he so badly wanted."

Maria invited Cousin Rollo to come up to the house for supper that evening. It had been a particularly busy day. Ruth, Cora and Linda worked hard in the kitchen and the dining room to keep all the daily visitors happily fed. Several of the regular customers who assembled every day for morning coffee on the porch were now volunteering to help run the lunchtime soup kitchen. Desmond served many customers in the vintage shop. Bella and Harriet happily spent the day sewing and singing and helping Desmond when extra help was necessary in the shop. Fred and Cousin Rollo busily occupied themselves in the grounds tidying things up after the easter egg hunt and trying to figure out what was to be done about the large gaping hole. Maria had spent her day pondering over the buried treasure and eventually directing her energy more purposefully into making a chocolate cake, a tasty vegetable stew and some homemade bread ready for supper with Cousin Rollo.

Maria loved the old house when it was so alive with visitors, it rang with noisy laughter and excitement. It had become a joyous place. However, in the silence of the late evening and the night time it took on an almost magical energy. Its walls were not only warm from the warmth of the hot Florida sun but warm from the love of the many visitors and regular customers who crossed the threshold who'd come to love and appreciate the old place. It had become a gathering place for friends, a community out outreach for the lonely and homeless and more than anything else a place of belonging, a home in every sense of the word. She looked around at the beautiful décor, the stained-glass windows and the lovely wood and smiled, "Cousin Rollo St. Eustace is a treasure, a place of love and acceptance. A far greater treasure than a handful of gold coins." Rollo flung back his head and laughed, "Maria we've created something truly special, a lifeboat if you will for these troubled times and it's a treasure indeed!"

After supper the old couple sat together and examined the seven gold coins and then they turned their attention to the old cigar box. As Maria gently fingered it Rollo began to tell her about Key West's rich cigar making history. "Of course, cigar making is highly skilled, workers served a long apprenticeship and the artisans made a good living. Tobacco leaves were imported from Cuba resulting in a strong authentic smoke. They made the cigars by hand and this included stripping, selecting and packing the tobacco that was then carefully rolled into the finished cigar. You know for decades the cigar making factories in Key West dominated the industry.

Maria, it all began nearly two hundred years ago in 1831 when William Wall built the first factory and as time went on more followed. The industry really flourished between 1870 and 1900. The Gato, Monte Cristo and Cortez Cigar Companies were well known but as the industry peaked in the 1880's and 1890's many more factories were constructed. In 1873 there were 15 factories employing 1,200 workers but by 1880, almost 3,000 people were working in 57 factories. The industry reached its peak in 1890 with 129 factories in operation and thousands of workers producing 100 million cigars that year.

The first Cuban to own and operate a major Key West cigar factory was, Eduardo Gato he was one of Key West's success stories. He quickly outgrew his first factory but he eventually purchased land on Simonton Street and built the largest cigar factory in the city. Surrounding the factory, he constructed cottages that he rented to his workers. The enclave became known as *Gatoville*. With his financial success he was able to build several luxurious homes for his wife Mercedes and himself. When he eventually returned to Cuba, Gato donated his house to the city as a hospital for the poor. It was named *Mercedes Hospital* and operated from 1911 until 1944."

Maria smiled, "Gato sounded like an honourable man who put his fortune to good use. Cousin Rollo, what happened to this lucrative industry and all those factories?" Rollo suddenly looked sad, "Maria, Key West, this interesting place at the end of the road, has always been a mixture of heaven and hell. There were fires and hurricanes, labour unrest and conflicts, the relocation of factories and workers to Tampa, and of course the growing popularity of fashionable cigarettes all led to the decline of Key West as Cigar City. Of course, the biggest blow was when Vincente Martinez Ybor moved his factory to Tampa in what is now known as *Ybor City* because it offered better infrastructure and communications."

Movement really began in 1886 when there was a great fire that swept through Key West, and unfortunately it destroyed many of the cigar factories. Apparently, it began in a coffee shop next to the *San Carlos Institute*, the heart of Cuban culture in Key West. There has always been firm speculation that the fire was started on purpose by arsonists sent by the Spanish empire attempting to undermine Key West citizens' support for Cuban independence. Cuban emigrants had found economic prosperity in Key West and their money helped to fund the Cuban revolution. The morning after the fire, there was a Spanish ram waiting to take on any unemployed Cuban cigar workers who wanted to return to Cuba. 400 workers returned at that time. What's even more interesting is the fact that Havana newspapers reportedly ran an article describing the great fire the day before it actually took place! The great fire burned for 12 hours over 50 acres, destroying most of the commercial area of the city, killing seven people, injuring 15 more, and the cost was one and half million dollars in property damage."

Maria continued to gently finger the old cigar box then she put the handful of gold coins back into their velvet purse. Looking extremely pale and weary she wished Cousin Rollo goodnight, tucked the box under her arm and climbed the stairs to retire for the night. Rollo cleared the dishes and locked up then made his way home reflecting upon the events of the day. He pondered over Key West's checkered history and heritage. He mused over the fortunes that could be made in the city at the end of the road together with the fear and possibility that sudden loss was somehow lurking in the shadows.

Maria was restless, she readied herself for bed and set the cigar box upon her nightstand. She fell asleep thinking about Pedro and his fortune and eventually the old man appeared perching himself at the bottom of her bed and muttering, "Los mejores puros de Pedro."

Maria sat up, nothing frightened the old wizened woman, she'd witnessed and become privy to so much over time. She reached out a hand of friendship and simply said, "Pedro please do tell me your story."

The old man coughed and smiled. "I grew up in the Cuban countryside. My family were poor farm hands and I was one of ten children. There was never enough money to feed all of us. Many days I would go hungry or visit neighbouring farms and steal whatever I could lay my hands on, out of necessity you understand. We led a simple life; farm work was hard and joyless. I witnessed my mother and father growing old before their time. Some of my brothers and sisters died, they weren't strong enough to fight the many illnesses that we faced. Poor nutrition, crowded living conditions and hard work all took their toll. I helped bury too many loved ones.

When I was sixteen, I decided to leave. To be perfectly honest I was selfish. I wanted a better life for myself, something different, toiling in the fields all day under the hot sun just wasn't for me. It certainly wasn't the life I dreamed of. I wanted adventure and to see more of the world. Of course, my parents found it difficult to forgive me. We weren't an educated family. I had little in the way of skills but I was young, reasonably healthy and above all else I was determined and driven. I made my way to Havana and befriended some of the fishermen down at the harbour.

Luis had his own sailing boat, *The Elena,* named after his wife. He took a gamble and said that he would teach me all that he knew. There were several other crew members, seasoned seafaring men, hardy and knowledgeable about the weather and fishing. I learnt a lot, how to sail, swim and dive, read the clouds, the tides and currents, the phases of the moon, and how to navigate by the stars. I also learnt where and when to fish. I grew in strength and confidence. Luis' wife even taught me how to read and write. They were good times. I felt safe and secure for several years then when I was twenty-two years old it suddenly all came to an end because influenza came to town.

It arrived like a thief in the night destroying our peace and prosperity and taking the lives of all the other crew members. Only Luis and I remained. He was distraught but insisted that he and I could manage *The Elena* because we needed to continue fishing. He said that his family's welfare and livelihood depended upon us and that's when he began to insist that we begin to take risks with the weather and to venture out into unknown waters. He was always hoping for a bigger, better catch.

The Elena really needed 5 or 6 deck hands; she was far too much for the two of us to handle. Luis knew it and I knew it too but he was so fearful that his family would starve so we continued to take chances. I remember that fateful day so very clearly. It was early March and the weather was good but I had a very bad feeling in the pit of my stomach when we set out. Luis insisted that we venture even further from home. He'd heard that the fishing was really good nearer to Key West and he insisted that we pack enough food and water for many days. We were 12 hours out and it was beginning to get dark when Luis unexpectantly took sick.

It came on so very suddenly. There was no warning. He complained of a really bad almost blinding headache and he began to vomit. He had a high fever and he said that his body really ached as if every bone was broken. Well, I really didn't know what to do. I tried to make him comfortable under some blankets down in our simple cabin and encouraged him to sip water but we had no medicine on board only bandages and Lugol's iodine solution for simple first aid emergencies.

The wind was getting up, the sea was choppy and rain had set in. I decided to reef the sails because *The Elena* was becoming much too difficult to handle. Within a few hours Luis was delirious and we were being tossed about. I was really frightened. I wanted to set out the anchor but I knew that the water was far too deep. I decided to try and turn back towards Cuba but the wind and current were against me and the wind became stronger, almost gale force. We were tossed about like a cork. In the end I took down the mainsail, kept the jib out, prayed and hoped for the best.

I really don't know how I got through that awful stormy night. At the break of dawn when the storm had dissipated and I had some light, I noticed that we were in really shallow water. I had no idea where we were but later when I had safely returned to Cuba, I worked out that we were probably in the area of The Rebecca Shoals.

These shoals lie about 42 miles west of Key West, 6.2 miles west of the Marquesas Keys and 31 miles east of the Dry Tortugas. They are a treacherous small coral bank in about 11 feet of water subject to strong currents and rough seas and surrounded by deep water in an area where the Atlantic Ocean and the Gulf of Mexico meet. Lt. George Meade made the first attempt to place a light on The Rebecca Shoals in 1854 but structures were washed away twice in 1855 while still being erected. It wasn't until 1886 that a lighthouse was finally successfully erected on the shoals. It was a 1 ½ - story square house set on high pilings and often impossible to land supplies or keepers at the lighthouse during bad weather.

I was so exhausted and decided to set down the anchor for a while. Luckily *The Elena* had a draught of only four feet. I was desperate to rest for a few hours before making a plan to return home. I checked on Luis; he was in a really bad state. I didn't like the way that he looked, his face was a deep red, almost purple. His fever was still raging and he was still delirious. I couldn't rouse him at all. I moistened his mouth with water, sponged his face and head and then exhaustion got the better of me and I collapsed in the cabin beside him. I woke up a few hours later, the hot sun was beating down and I knew that I needed to get some urgent help for Luis. I moistened his lips again, sponged his hot head and decided to jump overboard to cool myself down before pulling up the anchor and setting sail.

It was while I was in the shallow clear water and having a quick swim to cool myself down that I happened to look under the water and saw a small chest wedged in the coral. I was curious and dived down. It rested in about six feet of water. I'd heard many tales of pirates and all the treasure to be found in the waters around Key West and beyond. The old Cuban fishermen who frequented the harbour wall in Havana would often talk of such things. I thought that it was all just idle talk. The chest was heavy so I climbed back onto *The Elena* and grabbed some rope. Diving back in I made several attempts to get two ropes wound around the chest. I cut up my hands on the sharp coral trying to make them secure. When I clambered back on board my hands were bleeding but curiosity had got the better of me and along with the excitement and possibility of treasure, I didn't notice any pain at all. I seemed to have acquired super human strength as I hauled upon the two ropes and eventually pulled the small, heavy chest aboard. I went into the cabin to wash my hands in fresh water and to apply some Lugol's solution to my cuts. Once again, I gave Luis some water and sponged him down. I knew that I needed to get him help so the chest was left under a seat and I raised the sails and retrieved the anchor.

I think it was by sheer luck that the wind and currents were favourable and that I headed *The Elena* in the right direction. I continually scanned the horizon all day long for other vessels but there was nothing only sea birds and the occasional dolphin. As evening approached and I could see the stars I was able to navigate with confidence and finally I knew that I was headed on a course for Havana. Luis continued to alarm me he seemed comatose. He'd become pale and blue around his lips; he felt cold, his breathing was shallow and his pulse was weak and his strong burly body was unresponsive. I didn't know what to do other than to cover him with blankets and moisten his cold blue lips.

I sailed all night long and just as dawn was breaking, I eventually pulled into the safety of the Havana harbour. I quickly tied up at the stone quayside and went down into the cabin to check upon Luis before running for help. Much to my dismay, he seemed lifeless. There was a kindly woman with her husband taking their dog for an early morning walk along the quayside who agreed to come aboard and check upon Luis. She said that she knew something about medicine. She knelt down beside him and carefully checked him over then she turned to me and simply said, I'm so sorry, your friend has passed away. There's no pulse, he's not breathing. I don't remember much, it was an awful blow, such a shock. I was exhausted and I think I must have fainted. The kindly woman stayed with me while her husband went to fetch a local doctor who eventually took charge and made all the necessary arrangements to remove his corpse. The doctor told me that he'd probably died of the influenza that had recently ravaged through Havana and that I was not to blame.

I felt really guilty for a long time because I hadn't been able to save Luis. It was so difficult facing his family. His wife had always been so kind to me. She'd taught me how to read and write. Luis had been like a father. He'd taught me all that I needed to know about seafaring. I felt that I'd let him down, that I could have done more. It took me many years to feel good about myself again.

The mysterious chest sat under the seat in *The Elena* for a few days and quite forgotten. However, once Luis had been laid to rest in the cemetery, I returned to the boat to clean and tidy things up. His wife wanted to sell her immediately; she needed the money to support their family.

I knew that I was going to miss Luis because the past six years had been good ones. I had forged a new, happy life for myself. I'd made friends amongst her crew and it was difficult to come to terms with the fact that everyone was now in the cemetery. As I busied myself, I wondered what on earth I was going to do next. I had a little money saved, but only enough to pay for my lodging house for a few more weeks. Then I knew that I would be in dire trouble. It was time to find other employment. I did my best to ensure that *The Elena* was looking her very best by the end of that sad day. It was only as I was preparing to leave with a small bag of my own personal possessions and I was bidding my final farewell to *The Elena* that I suddenly remembered the sea chest hidden away under a seat. It was getting dark so I decided to carry it back to my lodgings. It was heavy but thankfully I didn't live too far away.

That night, after supper, I fiddled around with the lock. I had a few tools stashed away under my bed and after several hours I was able to prise it open. You can imagine my shock when I found myself looking at piles of shining gold coins wrapped in a heavy oilskin cloth. I yelled, "treasure!" I couldn't contain my excitement. I counted several hundred. That night I couldn't sleep because I was overcome with emotion. I knew there were traders in town that dealt with old coins so early the next morning I hid the chest under my bed and took a brisk walk into the market place with one of the gold coins hidden away in the depths of my pocket.

The elderly trader was curious, he wanted to know how I had come by such a coin and where I lived. I was wary and didn't tell him much. Luis had taught me how to be street smart because Havana was full of dangerous, unscrupulous people. The old man eventually confided that it was a Spanish doubloon made of 22 - karat gold and worth a lot of money. This was the moment when I knew I was suddenly rich and the world was my oyster. I would be able to travel, live in a nice home, own fine things and never again want for food. I was dizzy with excitement and I didn't even remember the walk back to my lodging house but I do recall that before I entered, I checked that I hadn't been followed. This was also the beginning of a constant habit that involved always looking over my shoulder. Seemingly overnight I had become suspicious and constantly vigilant. I was always on the lookout for someone who might attack me and steal my treasure.

In those early days I still acted with grace and integrity. I counted out little piles of seven coins and carefully distributed each pile of seven amongst Elena and the families of the other four crew members who had recently died from the influenza. Everyone was so grateful. Few questions were asked. I simply told them all that I had found a box when out fishing. I returned to my childhood home in the countryside and left seven coins with my elderly parents to feather their retirement. Then I set off to explore the world. I'd spoken with one of the large banks in Havana and had secured a safety deposit box. The bulk of my treasure was secretly stashed away and a handful of coins were exchanged for cash to fund my travels.

For three years I journeyed to foreign places. I ate rich food and stayed in fancy hotels and met lots of interesting people but after a while life became dull and boring and I yearned to settle down and establish a proper home. Finally, I decided to set up home in Key West. I transferred my fortune to a bank there and I purchased a large home in a quiet street off Duval. I was still young, only twenty-five.

Unfortunately, the treasure trove turned my head and led me into bad ways. Of course, it happened gradually. I'd become used to a lavish lifestyle and in the back of my mind I knew that one day the money would surely run out. I'd taken a liking to gambling, pretty women, whisky, good food, and fine cigars. Living the high life was a slippery slope. In my late twenties I became involved in a number of business ventures and made some extra money. I'd married but my wife eventually ran off with a younger man. I wasn't making good choices when it came to friends and partners. I really think I'd begun to lose my moral compass.

I'd turned forty years old when I decided to venture into the cigar making business. It was lucrative and of course my link with Cuba was particularly helpful. A lot of factories were being established; it was competitive. I was a hard taskmaster. My cigars were top quality but I'd become mean, I failed to treat my staff with kindness or respect. I cut corners to make a fast buck. I provided cottages for some of my workers but when they fell ill and weren't fit enough to work in my factory, I turned them out onto the street. I'd slowly developed a hard, greedy, unforgiving persona. People whispered about me behind my back and complained that I was a hard taskmaster and a wicked man. All the drink and smoking hadn't served me well. I became fat and suffered from painful afflictions. The doctors said I had gout, the rich man's disease. I developed a chronic cough, shortness of breath and every time I looked in the mirror, I saw a ruddy, wrinkled face that was bloated. I had lost my good looks and I felt wretched both inside and out.

By the time I was sixty years old I was an old sick man. I had no heirs and little left in the way of family to speak of. The money was running out and only a trickle of gold coins was left in the treasure chest. Then the big fire of 1886 happened. It destroyed so much of the Key West business district and it took my factory and my home with it. Lots of people lost their livelihoods that night. Many cigar factories and sponge warehouses were razed to the ground. Strong winds were blowing, which caused the fire to start up again even when it appeared to have been put out. Unfortunately, the city's only steam fire engine had been sent to New York for repair. Firefighters were only able to use less effective measures like hand pumpers. For me it was the last straw, I had neither the energy nor the passion to start again. I was feeling extremely depressed, the fire and loss had been a huge shock for me.

A business associate kindly took me in and said I could stay at his home until I got back on my feet but I knew deep in my heart that was extremely unlikely. About a week after the fire Luis came to me in a dream. He was standing by my bed. I hadn't forgotten him despite all the years that had passed. He'd been so kind to me, he'd set me on my way in life but all in all I knew that I hadn't made a good job of it. I'd not used the treasure wisely; I'd become a selfish man. I was far too self-indulgent. He reached out a hand and simply said, Pedro it's time. Set your affairs in order, bury what's left of your treasure and hopefully someone else in another time will make better use of the fortune. You have a band of friends waiting for you on the other side, all those men whose families you helped in those early days before your head got turned.

The dream was vivid and felt urgent. I knew that I was dying and it wouldn't be long before I was called away. The next day I went searching for a good spot to bury what was left. I eventually discovered a deserted home called Seaview and in the large grounds a monkey puzzle tree had recently been planted. I examined the site carefully and saw that a cave ran beside the tree and had opened up somewhat because of the planting. It seemed the ideal hiding place for the old sea chest. Seven gold coins were left and of course I planned to leave a note for the finder. It felt like the right thing to do. I went to my bank and collected the chest from their vault. I talked to the bank manager and told him that I was unwell and that what time I had remaining wouldn't be long. I'd left a will with instructions that the funds in my deposit account were to be sent to my only living brother and sister who still resided in Cuba.

That night I ventured out late under the cover of darkness with a spade borrowed from my friend's stable. I set about burying the chest. It was hard work. I wanted to ensure that it was buried deeply and kept well hidden. I toiled for about two hours finding it difficult to breathe and my chest really began to hurt. Eventually I returned home with muddy hands and feet.

I washed and slipped into bed happy, relieved and content that I had set things in order. I passed away in the middle of that night in my sleep. I don't think that my heart was up to all that heavy work. A doctor was called when the chamber maid found me late the next morning and he pronounced me dead, probably from a heart attack.

I've been waiting for the chest to be discovered because I want more than anything else for that money to be put to good use. I want it to make a difference and then I can truly rest. One of the coins, amongst those seven, is of tremendous value so please make sure that you take it to a reputable coin collector. That coin has the potential to do the best work."

Maria looked up and smiled. "Pedro, thank you for sharing your story. This lifetime is but one day in school. Remember your lessons for next time around. Don't make the same mistake. True treasure is found in helping others, reaching out with a hand of friendship, living a life of kindness and compassion. I think that you understand that now. I want to assure you that what treasure is left will be put to the best possible use and it will make a difference here in Key West to the people and to the community. I'm a woman of my word." Pedro smiled, he knew in his heart that his legacy was in good hands and he finally began to fade away knowing that he'd passed on the guardianship. His work was done and now he could finally rest.

Maria pondered upon her encounter then fell asleep knowing that there was much work to be done and that God had provided St Eustace with the necessary funds to make new future projects possible for the greater good. The next day she shared with Cousin Rollo her enlightening encounter with Pedro. Together they carefully examined all seven coins and indeed one of them was completely different. Cousin Rollo collected coins in his younger days and pointed out the significance of the doubloon design on six of them. "Maria, the cross struck on the reverse side symbolizes the Crusader's Cross. The stamped design signified the undivided union of the Catholic Church and the Spanish government during the 16th and 17th centuries. The reverse of the doubloon also depicted a lion and a castle to illustrate the provinces of Leon and Castile. The obverse shows the Hapsburg Shield which is the family emblem of the House of Hapsburg, the ancestral lineage of Queen Isabella and King Ferdinand of Spain." Maria poured studiously over the beautiful shiny gold coins. All of them were in excellent condition despite being buried underground for so long.

Eventually her attention turned to the seventh coin, definitely the odd one amongst the cache. It depicted an eagle surrounded my stars and engraved with the date 1787. As she carefully turned it over, she saw a lovely image of a mountain or perhaps a pyramid with the sun shining behind it and what looked like sea in the foreground. She noticed that there was a name clearly written spelling BRASHER. Cousin Rollo smiled, "Maria, I do believe that we have treasure indeed. If I'm not mistaken this is a Brasher Doubloon. Ephraim Brasher was a goldsmith and a silversmith highly regarded for his skills. His hallmark, which he not only stamped on his own coins but also on other coinage sent to him for assay proofing, was highly significant in the early United States. Brasher struck various coppers, in addition to a small quantity of gold coins few of which survive. The unique Brasher Doubloon was the first gold coin made for the United States. I recall that in 2021 Heritage Auctions sold one of them for $9.36 million, a world record for a gold coin sold in a public auction!" Maria nearly fell off her chair as she clutched the gold coin tightly. "Rollo that's treasure indeed and think about all the good that we can do with that kind of money!"

The coins were locked securely away in the large safe at St. Eustace and an emergency house meeting was called for that evening. Maria asked Ruth to prepare a simple supper for everyone at 7pm. Harriet and

Bella asked if Pastor Joe could come along too. Everyone sat anxiously around the large oak table in the sewing room speculating as to why they'd been called together. Linda was particularly excited and still muttered the word *treasure* continually under her breath. When the meal was over and the table had been cleared Maria looked around at the expectant faces and announced that she wanted to gather everyone together to share Pedro's story. She explained how he'd visited her in the night and recounted the story of his checkered life. "I want everyone gathered here to realize that Pedro has left St. Eustace a lifeline in these troubled times because his legacy will fund so many worthwhile projects for our growing community. It will enable us to truly flourish and I want you all to think about projects that we can discuss, research and possibly implement in the future."

Everyone was so excited and a burst of ideas were forthcoming and shared that very evening. Ruth shared how she was particularly worried about the amount of sugar and sweet things that St. Eustace currently offered. She argued that she wanted to change things and offer less sugar, more plant-based options and encourage visitors to eat healthier. "I'm really concerned about all the obese folk who come, it's not healthy we really should be setting more of an example. Perhaps we can hire an executive chef and more folk to help me out in the kitchen. There's plenty of local restaurants currently offering vegetarian food and trying to offer healthier options. Americans are addicted to and fuelled by sugar, we're all guilty and we need to make a change because everyone is so fat and sick!" Fred chimed in and suggested that better use could be made of the extensive grounds. "We can grow more of our own vegetables and ensure that they are raised organically; we can plant fruit bushes and trees; avocados and bananas and we can organize self-help classes to teach locals how to grow their own food. Of course, I'll need help from people who really know what they are doing in the garden."

Pastor Joe's hobby was trains. He made and collected model trains in his spare time. "I would like to see a model railway set up in the grounds of St. Eustace something to delight both locals and visitors alike. It'll provide plenty of focus and volunteer opportunities for the men folk who currently participate in the garage community. I can visualize in my mind's eye a model village depicting Key West back in historical times perhaps when Pedro was establishing his cigar factory. We could call it *Pedro's Town*. It'll keep his name, memory and the generosity of his treasure trove alive." Everyone smiled and agreed that Pastor Joe had come up with a grand idea because lots of folk could become involved and the children would absolutely love it. Desmond exclaimed, "We can even have Thomas the Tank Engine and his friends running on the tracks!"

Cora shared that she would like more to be done for the Key West homeless community. "I know that we currently offer the lunchtime soup kitchen and that it's a huge success. However, additional money could be put into offering even more healthy food for that needy community. In addition, I would love to see an out building constructed at the back of the big house that would offer toilets, showers, toiletries and clean towels. I also want to have a laundry room where they could come and wash their clothing and bedding. We could even have a clothing closet where donated clothes could be stored and folk can come and choose some new clothes for themselves too. I've read about such projects offered in other places." All agreed that once again this was a wonderful idea.

That night everyone began to venture home happy and with a glow in their hearts knowing that St. Eustace's future was secure and that great things would be happening in time all because of Pedro and his hidden gold. Desmond lingered behind at the front door as they departed and before leaving, he whispered to Maria, "I was so very sorry to hear Pedro's distressing story. I can't help thinking about him and how he felt so helpless when Luis became critically sick on the fishing boat with the flu. If only he'd known about homeopathic remedies, he may have been able to save his good friend and mentor's life. Certainly, *Belladonna* for the very high, delirious fever that came on so suddenly and *Carbo Veg* when his lips turned blue and he'd become cold and almost lifeless like a corpse. I've learnt so much since you encouraged me to look into alternative healing options and so much to personally thank you for, Maria."

Maria looked tired and wistful. "Desmond, we have so much to do. People need to be educated and to learn that there's many things available that can promote better health and even save lives and yes, I agree with you. If only Pedro had known about homeopathy, I'm sure that he might possibly have saved Luis. He must have been very fearful on that boat in the storm. It came up so suddenly and he alone had to navigate his way back to Havana. The Bach essences, particularly *Rock Rose* for terror, would have been helpful for any one facing such a situation and Pedro would have found *Chestnut Bud* helpful too. It's the Bach essence for those who fail to learn life's lessons and continually make the same mistake. He knew in the end that he hadn't chosen the best course in life and that he'd made so many mistakes. Then there's *Holly* the wonderful essence to open up the heart. He had a lot to learn. Hopefully he won't make the same mistake next time around and he'll live his next life with grace, compassion and make better choices." Desmond nodded in agreement and stepped out into the warm spring late evening air and smiled muttering to himself. "Life is good, I've found my home here at St. Eustace. It's become such a very special place."

Cousin Rollo and Maria eventually made the long drive north up towards Boca Raton on the east coast of Florida to consult with a rare gold coin dealer who'd come highly recommended. Arrangements were eventually made to sell four of Pedro's gold coins including the valuable Brasher Doubloon. Maria insisted upon keeping the remaining three coins because she felt deep down in her own inner knowing that at some time in the future they just might come in useful. With a sizeable fortune deposited in the bank and a wealth management company engaged to advise regarding the purchase of stocks and shares it all looked as if St. Eustace's future was secure. Maria sighed and one sunny day at the very beginning of June she smiled and announced to everyone gathered around the large oak table in the sewing room, "Friends, at long last we can begin to realize all of our plans, our hopes and our dreams. This old house is our home and now we can make it even better. Thanks to Pedro's legacy we can reach out to more folk desperate for our help and for our love.

On that note I've really wonderful news concerning Brenda. I know that you've all helped her on the road to recovery. For months now she's had friends from the St. Eustace community visit her daily and offer companionship. She's been for regular walks, people have aided with her diet, taken her shopping to the farmer's market, shown her how to cook healthy meals and ensured that she's been talking her vitamins and supplements. I know that she's done really well with the Bach flower essences especially *Bach Crab Apple* for cleansing and the homeopathic remedy *Natrum Sulph.* it's a great remedy to help to support the liver and detoxify and for someone who suffers from chronic asthma. Well, my friends, I'm absolutely delighted to report that according to her husband her brain is starting to recover and she's doing so much better. I think by the time that the fall comes along we might even be able to welcome her into the vintage shop to give Desmond a helping hand." Everyone was absolutely delighted because much hard work and dedication had been directed towards Brenda's needs. Their efforts had been so worthwhile. Now, she was reaping her rewards, Brenda was finally reclaiming her health. However, the St. Eustace folk knew that it had taken a village!

Royal Platinum Jubilee Tea Party

While Maria, Cousin Rollo and the rest of the St. Eustace team were celebrating their good fortune exciting happenings were also occurring across the vast Atlantic Ocean. 2022 heralded the 70th anniversary of Queen Elizabeth's accession to the throne. She'd become monarch at the age of 25, following the death of her father in the early hours of 6th February 1952. In the months leading up to the Jubilee Poppy was really busy navigating the flurry of celebrations set to take place in the Isle of Thanet. In her rare moments of down time, she often wondered what Maria was up to in Key West. Sometimes she would sigh as she collapsed back at Lookout Retreat after a busy day. She quietly yearned for Maria to return and help out even if it was just for a short while. All three shops were really busy as townsfolk came in seeking bargains from the 1950's. It seemed as if everyone wanted a 1950's vintage style frock ready to wear during the jubilee celebrations!

Over the first weekend in June the 96-year old's Platinum Jubilee was to be marked by four days of celebrations across the United Kingdom. Many of the events - including a pageant, Trooping of the Colour and a star-studded concert at Buckingham Palace - involved an outdoor element. Of course, the fickle weather so notorious in Great Britain, was always a cause for concern. Thankfully it proved to be mostly somewhat kind, sunny and mild for the special long weekend of celebrations. Many street parties were planned to take place locally and Poppy decided early on in her event planning calendar that she would do something special in the Madam Popoff Vintage Emporium situated on King Street, Margate. Of course, nowadays there was the little shop in Ramsgate and the bigger one in Broadstairs too but it was in Margate where her new life had really begun. After all it was in Margate where Poppy had learnt so much from the old, wizened, mysterious shopkeeper. It was the Margate shop that had always captured her heart and had set her upon her own healing journey. It was in Margate that Poppy had finally come to appreciate that she was indeed someone special.

Poppy planned a large tea party celebration for late afternoon on Sunday June 5th. The shop would be closed at 2 pm when a band of willing helpers were set to come in and help her to organize for a 4pm start. They had also kindly offered to bake cakes and scones and make delicate cucumber and smoked salmon sandwiches. Racks of clothing would be pushed to one side and the old sewing machine tables would be brought out. Poppy planned to cover them with the beautiful tablecloths that Dennis had embroidered with lovely flower designs back in the early 1950's as he lay in his garden shed recovering from pulmonary TB. Maria Popoff had accumulated a vast collection of elegant porcelain china. All sorts of odd pieces such as cups, saucers, dessert plates and teapots were stashed away in the back-room cupboards. These were well loved treasures that Maria had collected over the years and now they would grace the tables for a fine Royal Platinum Jubilee afternoon tea party. Ollie was set to bring his heavenly harp and Cedric would be accompanying him on the violin. Isadora was going to shop for appropriate bunting and even some cardboard cut outs of Her Majesty. Gertrude offered to hand write pretty invitations decorated with flags and crowns. In mid-May they were mailed to all the regular customers who frequented the Madam Popoff Vintage Emporiums across the local area. Aunt Flora even agreed to come and read the tea leaves and Mary was set to bring in Winston for the tea party as long as sausages were on the menu!

A few weeks before the big celebratory long weekend Poppy arrived very early one May morning at the King Street shop. She planned a major tidy up and to clean the large picture windows before she and Gertrude decorated them with Jubilee memorabilia. It was a beautiful morning, one of those special days when the air was fresh and the sky was just turning a soft pastel blue. The recently risen sun was warm and the noisy seagulls were wheeling around the fishing boats securely tied up beside the stone pier. Margate hadn't woken up yet and Poppy always savoured such special moments. It was times like these when she felt so blessed to be in Margate and so very thankful that she'd made the decision to leave London and embark upon a new life beside the sea when her dear Aunt Flora had beckoned. When the mysterious

Maria Popoff stepped out of the shadows and offered her gainful employment and a whole lot more Poppy began to realize that she had many broken pieces to mend. She began to understand that she'd much to learn in the safety of her new found security. She breathed a sigh of relief as she opened the door, she felt the warm embrace of the little town and its people in her heart and smiling she muttered to herself, "I'm home."

It was only when Jack the lad was settled upon his velvet cushion and she'd made a cup of coffee that she noticed a couple of discreet brown paper parcels left in the recess by the front door. Poppy sat down and carefully unwrapped the mysterious packages. One of them was packed tightly with frocks from the 1950-1970's eras. In the second parcel, amongst layers of faded tissue paper, she discovered a beautiful porcelain cake plate, a matching cup and saucer and what looked like a shaving mug. Upon careful examination she could see that they marked Queen Elizabeth's coronation in June of 1953. They were obviously well loved and in mint condition. As Poppy held the large cake plate decorated with Elizabeth's image to her heart she began to drift off to another time.

Muriel was a proud, well-dressed woman but underneath it all she was just a bored 1950's housewife. Her life was dull. It lacked both focus and purpose. She often felt like a ship adrift at sea without a rudder and wondered what her life was all about. Her husband, Wally, was extremely difficult. Although he was a successful businessman, he was an absolute pain to live with. He was bossy, critical and always liked things to be just so. He demanded that everything should be squeaky clean, neat and tidy in their well-kept bungalow overlooking the sea. He insisted that his dinner was ready and on the table at exactly six o'clock every evening as he walked through the door. After dinner he would sit and read the daily newspaper and then watch his favourite programs on their black and white television. He made little effort to converse with Muriel. Sadly, the love that had once upon a time drawn them together in their late teens, when they met at a local dance hall during the Second World War, had dissipated in the mundane hum drum of everyday post war life.

Muriel was thirty years old and just a few years older than the new queen at the time of the coronation. She'd been married for ten very long years but unlike the Royal Family they'd not been blessed with any children. By 1953 Muriel was at the end of her tether. She felt isolated and lonely because all of her friends from her school days and the local typing pool, where she'd worked from the age of sixteen until her marriage, had families of their own. They'd all moved on. Muriel was stuck at home. Wally insisted that his wife did not need to venture out to work. He insisted that work was a man's job and it was his role to support his wife and family. He would often chide Muriel when she brought the subject up. Cutting her short and getting red in the face and hot under his collar and raising his voice he yelled, "Muriel what will the people in my office say when they hear that you've returned back to work? It just isn't done with people like us. Think about our social standing. We'll be the target of local gossip and I'm having none of that! I've a well-paid job and there's absolutely no need for you to return to the typing pool."

Being childless Muriel was the odd one out amongst her group of friends. Invitations to social gatherings were few and far between as the years began to fly by because Muriel and Wally didn't fit the traditional family model of two or three children. They couldn't relate to the conversations that young parents often have when their children are growing up. Muriel knew nothing about breast versus bottle. She knew nothing about terry towelling nappies or the latest fads in weening. She wasn't familiar with the local nursery schools or which local school was best for primary age children.

Of course, the long-anticipated coronation was a welcome reprieve. It definitely added some colour to Muriel's dreary life. She would buy the *Woman and Home* magazine at the local newsagents and pour over all the stories featuring the Royal Family. The anticipated glamour, pomp and ceremony of the June 2nd coronation helped to take her mind off the drudgery of her own life. When Wally surprised her by announcing that he had booked a hotel for a few days up in London for the event Muriel felt that her life had suddenly taken a turn for the better. They were going to take the train and stay at a small place near Oxford Street making it easy to get up early on the big day and join the crowds lining The Mall. London would be full of well-wishers and Wally wanted to be sure that they would get a good view of the Gold State Coach as it headed out from Buckingham Palace towards Westminster Abbey. It was to be pulled by eight grey gelding horses.

Muriel was so excited and enchanted by it all, the anticipation and then at long last the train journey up to London on Monday June 1st. The small hotel was neat and clean and passed the test of Wally's eagle eyes. On the big day the couple joined crowds of well-wishers waving flags. Muriel looked up at wonder at the Union flags flying from the lampposts. As the coach eventually passed by Muriel even caught a glimpse of Her Majesty wearing the stunningly beautiful George 1V State Diadem. This is the crown depicted on stamps. It was made in 1820 and features roses, shamrocks and thistles with 1,333 diamonds and 169 pearls. Unfortunately, June 2nd was a cloudy, rainy day but that didn't take any of the magic out of this spectacularly historic occasion. Wally, always thoroughly prepared, had of course brought two large black umbrellas for them both just in case!

Of course, the young couple got swept away with the excitement and grandeur of this once in a life time event. Wally fully intended to boast about their outing to some of his work colleagues when he returned to the office and insisted upon buying a few pieces of coronation commemorative china. A fancy cake plate, cup and saucer were purchased for Muriel and a shaving mug for himself. As the exciting day began to draw to a close the couple went to one of the Lyons Corner House Tea Rooms for a slap up, celebratory late afternoon tea. In their heyday, Lyons had 250 Corner Houses in London. Muriel and Wally eventually wandered back to their small hotel situated just off Oxford Street and near to Selfridge's. They were both pleasantly weary and retired to bed early after spending an hour or so in the hotel's sitting room. They talked to other weary but excited tourists who'd ventured to London for the coronation and they all shared their memorable experiences.

The couple's small bedroom was located on the ground floor. There were two small windows opening onto a side alley. The room felt hot and stuffy so Muriel cracked one of the windows open a little before retiring. They fell asleep quickly but Muriel was eventually suddenly woken up by the urgent wailing cries of what sounded like a baby. Sitting up she looked at her bedside clock it was 3 am. Muriel crept over to the window and the cries became much louder. She gingerly opened the window as far as she was able and quickly determined that the noise seemed to be coming from one of the aluminium dustbins stored directly underneath the window. Wally was comatose and snoring loudly so Muriel plucked up courage and quickly dressed herself. She quietly closed the bedroom door and ventured down the dark corridor towards the hotel's front door. Wedging it open with a large book from a nearby bookcase, so that she wouldn't be locked out, Muriel stepped into the deserted street. Drawing a deep breath and continuing to pluck up courage she wandered around to the side of the hotel to where the dustbins were located. The crying had stopped so Muriel was uncertain which dustbin to check as there were several of them all lined up against the brick wall. It was dark but she just about made out the room with an open window and looked in the dustbin closest to that window. Muriel lifted the lid; it was dark and difficult to make out exactly what was inside but as she reached her hands down much to her surprise, she suddenly felt something very soft. The bundle stirred and let out a little whimper. Muriel quickly lifted the soft bundle out and there was a little baby wrapped up in a shabby woollen blanket! She gasped and then her motherly instincts took over. She reached back into the dustbin to ensure nothing else pertaining to the bundle was there then she hurried back into the safety of the hotel with the baby cradled safely in her arms.

Muriel knew that she couldn't return to her hotel room as Wally certainly wouldn't be amused at all. She opened the sitting room door, thankfully it was deserted. Everyone in the hotel seemed to be asleep. In the silence of the night, she turned on a table lamp in the empty room and sat down on the sofa. Muriel slowly began to examine the baby. She carefully unwrapped the faded, threadbare blanket and a tattered piece of paper drifted to the floor. The little baby was naked, it was a girl. She looked up at Muriel with wide eyes. She was fairly clean and seemed to be very young. Having no experience what so ever of babies Muriel really couldn't tell if she was new-born or a few weeks old. Wrapping her up again Muriel reached down to the floor and opened the scribbled note.

Finder's keepers!

I'm so very sorry BUT I just can't manage her.

I already have six children. My husband left and I'm on my own with no money or help to feed my children. I beg you to please take care of her. Bring her up as your own and tell her when she's old enough that her mother loved her but just couldn't manage.

Hopefully she'll understand.

Muriel began to cry. Here was a desperate woman with too many children but she and Wally had none. Life seemed to be so very unfair. She'd prayed every night for a baby for so many years and now it seemed that God had finally answered her prayers. As Muriel looked down at the tiny bundle she determined there and then that for once in her life Wally wouldn't be having his own way and that she would do everything that she could in order to keep this little girl. Muriel bent down and lovingly gave the baby a kiss and said, "I'm going to call you Queenie because it was the coronation that brought me to London and led me to you my little one." Muriel cuddled the little bundle and eventually curled up on the sofa and fell asleep with Queenie cradled in her arms.

Doris always set her alarm clock for 5 am because that gave her time to wash, dress and sort her hair out. She touched up her face with a dab of rouge, fine powder and a lick of the latest shade of pink Revlon lipstick. It was the new spring colour touted by the girls who served behind the cosmetic counter at Selfridges. Doris was a woman of routine. She always arrived in the kitchen at 5.30am sharp and spent the next hour preparing breakfast for the hotel guests. She would cover the ten tables in the dining room with freshly laundered crisp white tablecloths and set out the polished cutlery, china cups, saucers and side plates. Then she ventured into the adjoining kitchen and put the water on to heat in the large tea urn. She filled the milk jugs and sugar bowls, set out little pots of thick homemade orange marmalade and pats of bright yellow butter and finally she started to cook the porridge oats on her big aga stove. Once the oats were bubbling nicely away, she sliced the bread ready for making toast.

Bert usually made his appearance by six o'clock. He was a large, jolly man with a big beer belly that made his striped apron a tight fit. He liked to sing the latest popular songs as he would start to prepare the eggs, sausages and bacon. Breakfast was always served between 7 and 8.30 am. The middle-aged couple had a well-oiled routine. They'd run their successful business for almost ten years. It usually catered to businessmen working in the City of London but weekends were usually busy with tourists. They offered bed, breakfast and a set evening meal at a reasonable rate. Therefore, their hotel had gained a good reputation and was often full. Of course, the coronation meant even more business. Tourists had secured their room bookings as far back as the Christmas of 1952.

Doris came downstairs as the clock in the hallway chimed 5.30am and her eagle eyes immediately noticed the large old book obviously out of place and lying on the floor by the front door. When she'd locked up at 11 pm on June 2nd she knew that everything was in order and that all of her guests were in for the night. Then she noticed the door to the sitting room was slightly ajar. Doris popped her head around the door and was shocked to see Muriel fast asleep on the sofa and cradling what looked like a baby! Doris, in her surprise blurted out, "What the dickens is going on here?" As Muriel stirred and began to sit up bleary-eyed Doris recognized her and knew full well that she hadn't arrived with a baby. Actually, children weren't allowed in her establishment. Doris and Bert had always made it clear that they only catered to reputable businessmen and married couples on holiday who had no children. Doris married Bert when she was sixteen and immediately fell pregnant with twins. Their boy and girl were now thirty years old; they were long gone from the family home. When the couple established their hotel business, they decided that there were to be no children. They were noisy, unpredictable and often left a mess!

Alarmed and all in a fluster Doris sat on the sofa beside Muriel and peered into the tattered threadbare blanket. She saw a tiny head and what appeared to be a very young baby sleeping. By this time Muriel had really woken up and began to slowly recount the events of the night and handed Doris the scribbled note. Following careful scrutiny of the tattered note Doris announced with an air of authority that she must telephone the local police station immediately and call a doctor to come and examine the poor little waif. Muriel was hesitant, more than anything she wanted to keep the baby. "Muriel, we simply must notify the police and I'll find you a clean crisp tablecloth to wrap the little mite in." Doris insisted.

PC Gordon was a married man with a young family of his own. He'd been in the Metropolitan Constabulary for 10 years; he knew Doris and Bert and their hotel as it was located on his local beat. Sometimes he would stop in for shelter when it was pouring down with rain. Doris would ply him with tea and Bert's famous bacon sandwiches and keep him talking in the kitchen. She loved to hear all the local gossip and PC Gordon always knew exactly what was going on. His heart immediately melted when he arrived at the hotel. It was 6.15 am. Doris was behind with her breakfast preparations and was hastily laying the tables.

Bert had come downstairs and was hovering over the tiny baby wrapped in a crisp white cotton tablecloth and still sleeping in Muriel's arms as she sat on the sofa. PC Gordon had seen many things during his 10-year employment but when children were involved, he found his job difficult to cope with. Over his career he'd witnessed 6 such abandoned babies, here was number seven, a wee waif probably a week or so old. He pulled out his notebook, scrutinized the tattered note that Muriel had discovered and sighed. Turning to Muriel he gently said, "Muriel, you probably saved this baby's life. They're often left in dustbins or at bus stops or on the underground platform late at night. If they're not discovered within a few hours, they usually die of hypothermia, heat exhaustion or starvation. The sisters at the local convent take them in, care for their immediate needs and eventually, if the little one is lucky, social services place them with a foster family or a family willing to adopt them."

Muriel started to cry and began to tell the kind policemen her own story. "PC Gordon I'm desperate for a child. I would like to adopt this baby I've already called her Queenie because of the coronation. I feel that God led me to her, he's sent her as a gift to me. I was meant to find her. I've prayed for so many years for a child and the note clearly says *finder's keepers*." PC Gordon scratched his head and said, "Muriel you can't argue with the note. Yes, I agree it does indeed say *finder's keepers.* However, this is very irregular. Couples have to be vetted, there's a whole procedure for folk who want to adopt. My wife's sister can't have children and a few years ago she and her husband had to go through the whole process. It takes time. You simply can't take the train home with this babe in your arms as if you just bought her from a fancy London store! Rest assured the sisters are kind and a local doctor will look her over." Smiling and putting his big hand on her shoulder he continued. "Muriel, I can certainly put in a good word and see if you can visit the convent later today and talk things over with Mother Angelica. You can explain your situation. I know that the sisters have many babies currently requiring adoption. If the paper work goes well I think there's a really good chance that in a few weeks' time you may be able to take tiny Queenie home. I'll telephone the hotel once I've talked with Mother Angelica. Of course, she'll want to meet your husband too and ensure that the baby is going to a home with two loving and dedicated parents."

Muriel dried her eyes, kissed Queenie goodbye and placed her in the burly policeman's capable arms. It was 7.30am. The tempting smell of cooked bacon and sausages was whiffing out into the hallway from the kitchen. Bert had wrapped up a warm bacon roll in grease proof paper and pushed it into PC Gordon's tunic pocket as he was leaving the hotel with Queenie. The hotel was beginning to wake up and a few guests had already entered the dining room. Muriel was exhausted both emotionally and physically. She was still sitting on the sofa thinking about what she could possibly say to Wally when she caught sight of him out of the corner of her eye. Looking happy and eager for a hearty breakfast he simply thought that Muriel had woken up early and had come to read her magazine in the sitting room.

Muriel knew that her difficult husband needed food before she could possibly broach anything of importance. She dutifully followed him into the dining room, poured him a cup of tea, buttered several pieces of toast and spread them with marmalade. Then she watched him enthusiastically tuck into a plate full of scrambled eggs, sausage and bacon. Unfortunately, before she had time to tell her story Doris had sauntered over to their table and asked where PC Gordon had taken the baby. Wally put down his fork and looking most surprised he enquired, "Muriel, what baby?"

A terrible feeling of utter dread suddenly came over Muriel but she slowly summoned the courage and found the right words to tell her husband all about baby Queenie. What Muriel hadn't anticipated was Wally's unusual response. Much to her surprise and delight he actually agreed to accompany her to the convent to meet and talk with Mother Angelica. Deep down Wally had known for a long time now that his marriage was in serious trouble. He knew that his wife was desperate for a child. He knew how depressed and unhappy she'd become and he feared losing her. He also knew that if he was to get on in his office and achieve senior management, he had to have a wife. It certainly wouldn't look good amongst his peers if his wife left him or worse still, if she had a mental breakdown or even committed suicide.

The young couple spent that morning wandering up and down Oxford Street window shopping. Then they headed over to St James Park to feed the ducks, sit down and relax whilst enjoying a pot of tea and a sandwich at a nearby café. It was almost 3pm before they returned to their hotel. Doris had been anxiously waiting for their return because the convent had telephoned shortly after lunch and requested that Wally and Muriel visit and take tea with Mother Angelica at 4 pm. Muriel's heart began to flutter as she quickly changed her clothes, combed her hair and put on some lipstick. Wally took a clean neatly ironed shirt out of his case and donned his favourite tie. Doris had walking directions to the convent ready and assured them that it was only ten minutes away so there was absolutely no reason why they wouldn't arrive at the appointed time. As they were leaving Doris shouted, "Mother Angelica is very particular so mind your p's and q's!"

The convent was a large imposing grey stone building surrounded by a high wall. They entered through a large wrought iron gate that creaked as it swung shut. There were a number of trees in the garden and some of them were in blossom. The last of the tulips were still flowering and the iris beds were about to burst forth. A young nun with a rosy face and dressed in a long black habit greeted them at the door and summoned them into the cavernous interior. She introduced herself as Sister Veronica and told them that she would take them to Mother Angelica's study. Muriel immediately noticed a beautiful statue of Mother Mary resplendent in blue and white and cradling baby Jesus in her arms. She had a circle of silver stars suspended above her head. Muriel smiled and immediately felt reassured despite the intimidating building, the hushed tones and the unfamiliar sight of nuns walking by in their black habits with their heads bowed.

Much to their relief Mother Angelica greeted them with a broad smile and a friendly, warm handshake. She introduced Mrs. Brown from Social Services who rose from her comfortable arm chair and smiled.

Turning to address Muriel Mother Angelica said, "PC Gordon has shared your story. Do sit down, tea will be served soon. You'll be pleased to know that baby Queenie is in the nursery. She has taken a bottle feed from one of the sisters and we've found some nice clothes for her. The local doctor stopped by at lunchtime and gave her a good looking over and pronounced her in excellent health. He has estimated that she's about one week old. Mrs. Brown is here to talk through the whole adoption process and has some papers for you to look over and sign. Of course, there'll be some back ground checks, that sort of thing but we're thinking that if all is well you should be able to take baby Queenie home in three- or four-weeks' time. This will give you both time to prepare a nursery and to purchase all of the basic baby necessities that you'll need." Muriel gasped with delight she couldn't believe what she was hearing. It all seemed like one big fairy tale. Mother Angelica suddenly looked sad and pensive, "Muriel, tragically we have so many unwanted babies here. However, PC Gordon put in a very good word for you both and assured me that Queenie would be going to a good home and that we needed to sort things out quickly while you were both still here in London."

Early that evening after tea, scones and cakes the couple made their way back to the hotel. Muriel had a spring in her step. She realized that her life had just changed forever.

Indeed, it had, neither Muriel nor Wally remembered the train journey back to Margate the following day and the next few weeks went by in a whirl. They shared their exciting news with their family. Muriel called old friends from the typing pool and Wally mentioned things to his colleagues in the office. Friends, neighbours and relatives were all very excited for the young couple and enchanted by what seemed to be a fairy tale story. Several old friends sorted through their cupboards and donated baby clothes and necessary nursery equipment. Some of the older ladies living in their neighbourhood insisted upon knitting pretty outfits for baby Queenie. Wally insisted that his daughter should have a brand new Silver Cross pram. One just like that used by the royal babies as their nanny had pushed them around in the London parks.

When baby Queenie eventually came home to Margate in early July of 1953 the local paper sent photographers and a journalist to report upon her story. Of course, Wally revelled in all of the attention. Muriel simply smiled and thanked God because at long last she had her baby and all was now well in her world. Queenie was lucky, she was coming home to a comfortable bungalow overlooking the sea and parents who would come to love her dearly and dote upon their only child.

Muriel now had a new focus in her life, a reason to get out of bed every day. She decided to learn how to sew. Wally kindly bought her a sewing machine for her Christmas present in 1953 and she signed up for Mrs. Rodwell's popular sewing classes held on a Friday night in Hawley Square, Margate at The Thanet School of Art. Wally would come home early that evening and baby sit his daughter while Muriel learnt useful dressmaking skills and made new friends. Queenie brought a lot of joy into the household. Muriel was always out and about taking her to the park or to the beach. Sometimes they would meet friends at the Lyons Tea Rooms on Margate High Street for a treat after she'd taken Queenie shopping. By the time that she was three years old Queenie had grown a mop on ginger curls and was ready to start dancing classes at Monty and Bunty's successful dance school.

When she was four years old, they purchased a puppy, a corgi, the breed that Her Majesty adored. The puppy brought yet more excitement and change into the household and they all started to have a lot of fun as a family. Gradually, over time, Wally slowly began to soften, he became considerably more flexible, less bossy, more centred upon helping others and less interested in his image and getting ahead in his office. Queenie brought stability to his marriage and at long last he too began to feel complete and truly happy with his life.

The coronation china, purchased on that magical day back in June 1953, graced the family's sideboard. Every year Muriel would carefully wash the fine porcelain cake plate, cup, saucer and shaving mug and pore over the image of Queen Elizabeth. The china always took her immediately back to the events of that auspicious night when she'd heard a baby crying under her window. Queenie went on to develop her dancing skills and eventually became a ballerina. In time she married and had a family of her own.

When her parents peacefully passed away in their late 80's, amongst many other things, she inherited the coronation china. It was when Queenie had turned eighteen years old that Muriel had finally plucked up courage and shared the story of her adopted daughter's beginnings. Therefore, when Queenie eventually became the coronation china's guardian, she too had a very special place for it in her heart. However, many years later unfortunately the china became lost or perhaps this was the fine porcelain's destiny.

It all happened in late May of 2022. Queenie was packing up her parents' bungalow. She'd inherited her childhood home when they'd passed away and she'd used it for the best part of fifteen years as a summer weekend getaway. It was the ideal place for her to retreat to when it became too hot in London where she'd been living and working for most of her adult years. Now that she was almost seventy years old, she planned to retire. Her daughter lived in Cornwall and wanted Queenie and her husband to relocate to that area so that they could all be near each other. Now it was sadly time to sell the little family bungalow overlooking the sea. Property in Margate was selling quickly and for a very good price too. Margate was definitely up and coming. A growing number of affluent and well-educated young couples had already relocated or were currently in the process of looking to purchase a property. Following two difficult years of Covid-19 many people had become accustomed to working online and had seen the benefit of such flexibility. Larger houses, clean air and living beside the sea was a big draw especially if there were ever to be more lockdowns in the future! After all, the local Thanet area, had beautiful sandy beaches, clean air and a developing economy focused upon young people with money in their pockets. There'd been an escalation in the growth of a number of new establishments. Kitsch boutiques, cafes, restaurants, bars, art galleries and culture were particularly attractive to the hipster crowd and drew them to the area. Margate was quickly becoming The Place to live and to be seen!

The neat little bungalow commanded an amazing sea view and no one was really surprised when it quickly sold. Although she'd tried to prepare herself for this painful moment Queenie was extremely sad and found it difficult to hold back her tears. The sale marked the passing of time. It marked the closure of many important chapters in her life. It had always brought back so many pleasant memories from her childhood and the enduring love and dedication of her adoptive parents. However, deep in her heart she knew it was time. Queenie had finally come to realize that this happy little place needed another family. It needed others who would enjoy the view and create their own fond memories. She still had a couple of old school friends living locally who graciously volunteered to help her sort through the home. Following a few video calls the three ladies hastily arranged and advertised a morning yard sale to sell the many things that Queenie had agreed to part with.

The yard sale proved to be most successful. Business was brisk. Thankfully there was no rain in the forecast! The weather was bright, sunny and warm drawing many nosey neighbours out to take a look. They'd mainly stopped by for a chat, to reminisce and to say goodbye to Queenie. Several elderly ladies, well into their nineties, shared their fond memories of Wally and Muriel and remembered tales of baby Queenie growing up.

After lunch Queenie and her friends worked with purpose to clear away what was left. She'd arranged a cleaning company to come by the next day to give the bungalow a thorough going over so that it would be ready to welcome its new occupants. Her husband arrived at 3 pm with a hire van to help out. Remnants from the yard sale were to be donated to charity. Other things such as a few pieces of sentimental furniture were to be packed into the van to take up to their London residence and eventually onto their new home in Cornwall. It was in all the hectic comings and goings of that sunny afternoon that the carefully packed coronation china was put into the wrong pile of things set aside.

Jean, Queenie's good friend from childhood, agreed to take things in her car to a local charity shop and she knew that there were a few clothes amongst the things set aside that might be appreciated by the staff at The Madam Popoff Vintage Emporium in King Street. This is how the coronation china ended up in Poppy's hands. Several days passed before a distressed Queenie discovered that her adoptive parents very precious coronation china was actually missing and by this time it was all too late. Queenie was forced to sadly accept that the link with the most crucial chapter of her life was finally closed. However, before finally letting go, she'd spent several nights lying in bed late at night wondering if she should return to Margate and visit all the charity shops searching for the china.

It was a memorable dream that finally had helped to set her mind at rest and to bring about closure. Queenie found herself back in the little bungalow. She was seated at the dining room table near the big picture window overlooking the sea. Muriel and Wally were also sitting there with an old, wizened lady who'd stopped by with homemade chocolate cake. The old lady was friendly and seemed to know Muriel and Wally. However, she was drinking tea from the coronation china and happily eating cake off the coronation cake plate. Queenie thought to herself how audacious! The coronation china was sacred. It had never been used for its intended purpose. For her entire life it had always graced the sideboard. As she'd grown up Muriel and Wally had always chastised her and told her never to touch the china. She had constantly been instructed only to look and never to touch. Her mother reverently removed it once a year and carefully washed and dried it. When her parents passed away Queenie had taken up the mantle of guardianship and had dutifully followed the once a year washing routine. Queenie just couldn't believe her eyes and more surprising still was the fact that her parents apparently were taking no notice. They didn't seem to mind at all! The three of them were engaged in animated conversation. Sitting at the table perplexed and not knowing how to respond appropriately the old lady suddenly turned and addressed her. She seemed to have sensed Queenie's shock and utter dismay. Wally and Muriel looked on as the old woman drew in a deep breath and then spoke with clarity and authority.

"Queenie, it's high time for everyone to move on. Muriel and Wally are happy and in a different place now. They love you; they always have. They want the best for you and one day they'll be waiting for you to come and join them. Sometimes truly moving on means letting go of the past, moving on to new things, new places, new opportunities and new memories, creating your own special memories. Soon their little bungalow will be in others hands. The coronation china was meant to be used and loved. However, it was part of their own special memories because it marked the memory of the day that your mother found you and she and Wally agreed to give you a wonderful home. Let the china go. Let it find a new home now. Let it find people who will love it just as much but in a different way. Let it be used by folk that will eat and drink from it and celebrate the amazing life and legacy of Queen Elizabeth."

With the ending of those profound words the old woman faded away. Muriel blew her daughter a kiss as she and Wally quickly faded away too leaving Queenie alone with her own thoughts. Then she suddenly woke up. Her pillow was wet from the tears that had gently fallen as everyone had faded. Queenie realized that she'd been given permission to leave things alone. She was ready to begin her new life in Cornwall.

Poppy opened her eyes; tears were flowing down her cheeks too as she gently fingered the fine porcelain china. She turned to Jack the Lad and stroking his silky coat she simply muttered, "quite a story!" Suddenly, out of the corner of her eye, she caught sight of two ladies anxiously waiting on the doorstep. Glancing at her watch she realized it was time to open up for business. There was little time to reflect that particular day because business was brisk. However, that night as all was quiet and still and as she lay in bed at Lookout Retreat, she thought about Muriel and Wally and that eventful coronation night. She wondered what would have happened if Muriel hadn't acted when she'd heard the baby crying. Poppy felt that some kind of unseen force must surely have drawn Wally and Muriel to that particular hotel. She then sadly reflected upon all the babies who had never made it into the arms of someone who cared, the undiscovered abandoned babies left to die. Then her mind wandered to those who grew up in large institutions and were never fortunate enough to experience life growing up in a loving family home.

Her mind slowly turned to Dr. Bach and his 38 flower remedies and she began to reflect upon some remedies that might have helped the childless young couple. Poppy recalled that Dr. Bach completed his important work not long before his untimely death in 1936. Her active mind reflected upon *Bach Rock Water* for Wally. Initially, before baby Queenie came along and changed the household dynamics, he seemed to have very high standards. He worked diligently and appeared to be most inflexible, a man of routine, particularly hard on himself. Wally certainly insisted that things were done to his own special liking. Poppy also thought that *Bach Vine* would have been helpful too because he liked to dominate others. *Vine* folk tend to be very capable, gifted and ambitious, thinking that they know better than others and they put other people down.

She thought how depressed and lonely Muriel had been stuck at home with no friends, a controlling husband who wouldn't let her work and her own unfulfilled need for a child. Before the excitement and glamour of the coronation she must have been at her wit's end. Poppy thought that maybe *Bach Gorse* would have been helpful at that particular time in her life because it seemed to be a good flower for feelings of hopelessness and despair. She definitely felt that there was no light at the end of the tunnel. After 10 long years of marriage and with no baby on the horizon she felt there was no hope and was about to give up.

Poppy smiled as she thought about baby Queenie who finally brought sunshine into Muriel's life. Wally changed before her eyes; he began to soften as the new baby helped to save their marriage. Finally, she reflected upon Queenie's life and what a lucky baby she'd been. Her loving, adoptive parents were such a blessing and a gift. It wasn't surprising that she'd found it difficult to come to terms with the loss of the coronation china as it brought back such fond memories of her parents and of her idyllic childhood living beside the sea. Poppy remembered that *Bach Honeysuckle* was a good flower for those who are over-attached to past memories, perhaps of much happier days. On the other hand, *Honeysuckle* may also be useful for people who are unable to get over unhappy past experiences. *Honeysuckle* folk may find it difficult to get over the passing of deceased relatives whom they loved dearly and now they find themselves revisiting the past all of the time.

Poppy smiled, she felt so very grateful for all of Dr. Bach's remarkable work and his teachings. Her new found knowledge had made it possible for her to offer some help so many unhappy, sick customers with these Bach flowers. She fondly recalled the day that she discovered his little tattered booklet describing *The Twelve Healers* in a pile of donated dressmaking patterns and magazines. She recalled how it had sat upon the old oak counter top until she, the student, was indeed ready to receive such an amazing gift. Before falling asleep her mind wandered yet again to Maria Popoff. Poppy constantly deliberated whether the wizened shop keeper might actually be an angel, or was she a magician? On the other hand, perhaps she was simply a wise old-time traveller? However, whatever Maria was Poppy knew that she missed her mystical presence, her all seeing eyes and her guiding hand. She really hoped that her guide, her mentor and her best friend would return one day soon from far away Key West.

The next few weeks were busy in the run up to the Platinum Jubilee. Poppy shared her remarkable coronation china story with Gertrude. They decided that the exquisite china would help to make a perfect window display, after all they'd planned to do something special to mark the historic occasion. Poppy dressed two of the shop mannequins up in some beautiful 1950's vintage clothes that were hanging upon a rack in the back room. She'd saved these elegant outfits for such an occasion. They'd been left on the doorstep in a large dustbin sack along with some other clothes about a year ago and she felt that one day they might come in useful. Gertrude found matching hats, handbags and gloves all from the 1950's era to complete the scene. Poppy brought two chairs from Lookout Retreat and a little coffee table. The well-dressed mannequins were carefully propped up on the upright chairs and Queenie's beautiful coronation china was laid out on a pretty white lace table cloth. Poppy also brought in a few extra pieces to complete the tea party setting from Aunt Flora's special china cabinet. Isadora's young niece liked to play shops and conveniently had a collection of realistic looking plastic fruit, cake and other foods that she was willing to lend for the window display. Poppy was able to add these to the coffee table and create an attractive 1950's scene. The window was finished by hanging very old union flags that Cedric had recently discovered stored away in the rafters of his garage.

Everyone was excited as the Jubilee long weekend approached. When she returned to Lookout Retreat after a busy day at the shop Poppy and Aunt Flora enjoyed following all the commentary on the television. Margate was bustling with visitors, there were street parties and celebration bunting everywhere. One evening she took her elderly aunt down to the Margate Sands to watch the magnificent firework display. Eventually Sunday arrived, the much-anticipated tea party day! Poppy felt so much gratitude for all those who had graciously volunteered to help. There were all the men folk who helped move the furniture, pushing racks of clothing aside so there was plenty of space for the sewing machine tables. She felt really thankful for all the ladies who'd volunteered to make fancy fairy cakes, scones and sandwiches.

Bill arrived to help out. He'd arranged to borrow a large tea urn from his local radio amateur enthusiasts club. Bill headed for the kitchen to set the urn up. Poppy and Bill had been stepping out together for almost a year now. Poppy smiled as he busied himself with chores and she reflected upon just how much she'd grown to love this dashing silver haired man.

Regular customers from around the local area started to arrive shortly after 4pm. Many of them had dressed in 1950's fashion. Mary arrived with Winston and Aunt Flora stepped out of a taxi holding Sir Humphrey, her darling little chihuahua, cradled securely in her arms. Cedric and Ollie were already playing to the excited gathering. A small table and two armchairs had been set aside for Aunt Flora so that she could read the tea leaves for the curious and adventurous. It was whilst everyone was tucking into delicate salmon and cucumber sandwiches and pouring Earl Grey tea from fancy china teapots that Maria Popoff made a sudden surprise appearance. It seemed that she just appeared from out of nowhere stepping into the middle of the party from behind the large costume mirror at the back of the shop. Everyone gasped as the wizened, portly lady smiled, gave a royal wave and sat down in the armchair next to Aunt Flora. Poppy sighed and muttered to herself, "Maria heard my prayers. I'm so very glad that she came to join us. Our party is now complete."

It was in all the joy and excitement of celebrating Her Majesty's historic milestone that Bill proposed to Poppy. He'd visited SH Cutting the local jeweller in Margate Old Town Marketplace a few days previously and had picked out a beautiful heart shaped sapphire ring surrounded by diamonds. Poppy, with a slice of chocolate cake in hand, couldn't believe her eyes when he'd risen from his chair and had got down on bended knee to propose. Everyone else also looked on with surprise and joy. They put their china teacups down and began to clap as he asked Poppy to marry him. With baited breath they all waited for her answer. Of course, it was *yes*, how could it have been anything else? Poppy had fallen head-over-heels with this kind, gracious and intelligent widower who was crazy about her and old radios!

References

In writing this book, I've referred to historical events. This information has been gathered from several sites, primarily Wikipedia. Here are the other sites:

Buried Treasure
www.2-clicks-coins.com

Wartime
www.earlyradiohistory.us
history.navy.mil
https://sanctuaries.noaa.gov/news/may18/world-war-i-on-the-homefront.html

This book by Reilly and Homan was used to gather historical information and events that occurred in Key West:

Homan, L., Reilly, T. (2000). *Images of America: Key West.* Arcadia Publishing.

The following books were used for information on Bach Flower Essences:

Scheffer, M. (2001). *The Encyclopaedia of Bach Flower Therapy.* Healing Arts Press

Wigmore publications Ltd. (2003) *The 38 Bach Flower Essences*

Sally's Pictures of Key West

Basilica of St. Mary Star of the Sea (left) and the Hurricane Grotto

Historic Eduardo Gato Cigar Factory Building (left) and the San
Carlos Institute Museum

Memorial to the US Battleship Maine in the Key West Cemetery (left)

CPSIA information can be obtained
at www.ICGtesting.com
Printed in the USA
BVHW071334150223
658524BV00007B/78

9 798885 312844